Ann Mears.

Upper IV

Autumn Term
1942.

High School,
Shrewsbury.

THE HERITAGE OF LITERATURE SERIES

Section A **1s. 6d.**   Section B **2s.**

The Heritage of Literature Series

SECTION A NO. 19

THE POETS' WAY
STAGE III

THE POETS' PATH . 1s. 6d.
In Two Parts, 10d. each

THE POETS' WAY

STAGE I . . . . 1s. 6d.

STAGE II . . . . 1s. 6d.

STAGE III . . . . 1s. 6d.

Stages I and II in one volume
2s. 6d.

THE POETS' WAY
STAGE III

SELECTED BY

E. W. PARKER, M.C.

LONGMANS, GREEN AND CO.

LONDON · NEW YORK · TORONTO

LONGMANS, GREEN AND CO. LTD.
39 PATERNOSTER ROW, LONDON, E.C.4
6 OLD COURT HOUSE STREET, CALCUTTA
53 NICOL ROAD, BOMBAY
36A MOUNT ROAD, MADRAS

LONGMANS, GREEN AND CO.
114 FIFTH AVENUE, NEW YORK
221 EAST 20TH STREET, CHICAGO
88 TREMONT STREET, BOSTON

LONGMANS, GREEN AND CO.
215 VICTORIA STREET, TORONTO

First published 1937

PRINTED IN GREAT BRITAIN BY
NORTHUMBERLAND PRESS LIMITED
NEWCASTLE UPON TYNE

FOREWORD

THE present book is a continuation of *The Poets' Path* and *The Poets' Way*, Stages I and II, and the success of the earlier volumes must be my excuse for adding another. Each book in the series provides plenty of varied material for one year's work, and, between them, the four volumes offer a large and representative selection of over 300 poems, both old and new. Not the least of the advantages that may be claimed for them is the avoidance of that tiresome duplication of poems which is inevitable when different anthologies are used at each stage of the work.

A quick glance at the contents will show that this book contains an even larger proportion of poems that are the work of contemporary poets. A more careful scrutiny will reveal the fact that most of the poems here are of a factual, descriptive, striking or clear-cut nature, and that many of them tell an interesting story. My reason for selecting such poems is that I have felt that they will give pleasure and arouse interest at a stage when lyrical poetry, written for those whose sentiments are mature, would make but little appeal. In this book, therefore, there are plenty of tales of vigorous action, and interesting descriptions of ships, railway trains, reptiles, birds and beasts, and of people and places. In addition, some poems which show the poet in a serious mood are included, as well as others in a lighter and humorous vein.

Throughout this series, my friend, Dr. Gurrey, has generously given me the benefit of his experience. I should like to acknowledge his kindness in helping me by criticizing the present volume, and by making valuable suggestions that I have gladly adopted. I should also like to thank the owners of copyright material for permission to use the poems that are reprinted in this collection.

Mr. J. Redwood Anderson for "The Crane" from *The Vortex*, published by Messrs. Victor Gollancz Ltd.; Mr. Martin Armstrong for "Miss Thompson Goes Shopping" and "The Buzzards" from *The Buzzards and Other Poems*, published by Messrs. Martin Secker & Warburg Ltd.; Mr. Laurence Binyon for "The Little Dancers"; The Clarendon Press, Oxford, for stanzas from "Eros and Psyche" from *The Poetical Works of Robert Bridges*; Messrs. R. Cobden-Sanderson Ltd. for "The Idlers" and "Mole-Catcher" from *Poems* by Edmund Blunden, for "Merry Maid," "Market Day" and "Farmer's Boy" from *Poems of John Clare*, edited by Edmund Blunden and Alan Porter, and for "Milk for the Cat" by Harold Monro; Messrs. Constable & Co. Ltd. for "Woods of Westermain" from *Selected Poems* by George Meredith; Mr. Walter de la Mare for "Sam" from *Poems 1901-1918*, published by Messrs. Constable & Co. Ltd.; Messrs. Gerald Duckworth & Co. Ltd. for "Tarantella" from *Sonnets and Verse* and "Hildebrand" from *Cautionary Tales*, by Hilaire Belloc; Messrs. Faber & Faber Ltd. for "Horses on the Camargue" and "Choosing a Mast" from *Adamastor* by Roy Campbell, for "The Journey of the Magi" from *Poems 1909-1925* by T. S. Eliot, and for "The Express" from *Poems* by Stephen Spender; Mrs. J. E. Flecker and Messrs. Martin Secker & Warburg Ltd. for the Prologue and Epilogue to "The Golden Journey to Samarkand" from *Collected Poems* by J. E. Flecker; Mr. W. W. Gibson and Messrs. Macmillan & Co. Ltd. for "The Parrots" and "Hands" from *Collected Poems 1905-1925*; Mr. Ralph Hodgson and Messrs. Macmillan & Co. Ltd. for "The Bells of Heaven" from *Poems*; Mrs. Rudyard Kipling and Messrs. Macmillan & Co. Ltd. for "The Way Through the Woods" from *Rewards and Fairies* by Rudyard Kipling; Messrs. John Lane The Bodley Head Ltd. for "A Cinque Port" by John Davidson; Mrs. Frieda Lawrence and

Messrs. Wm. Heinemann Ltd. for " Snake " from *Collected Poems,* Vol. II by D. H. Lawrence; Mr. John Masefield for stanzas from " Dauber " reprinted from *The Collected Poems of John Masefield,* published by Messrs. Wm. Heinemann Ltd.; Mr. John Murray for " London to Paris " from *Many Mansions* by Lord Gorell; The Oxford University Press for " Edom o' Gordon " and " The Douglas Tragedy " from *The Oxford Book of Ballads*; Mr. E. V. Rieu and Messrs. Methuen & Co. Ltd. for " A Musical At-Home " and " Sir Smasham Uppe " from *Cuckoo Calling*; The Hon. Victoria Sackville-West for three extracts from " The Land," published by the Hogarth Press; Mr. Siegfried Sassoon for " Morning Express " from *The Old Huntsman and Other Poems,* published by Messrs. Wm. Heinemann Ltd.; Messrs. Sidgwick & Jackson Ltd. for " The Waggoner " from *Poems* by Edmund Blunden, for " In Lady Street " from *Collected Poems* by John Drinkwater, and for " The Bridge " from *Walls and Hedges* by J. Redwood Anderson; Mr. James Stephens and Messrs. Macmillan & Co. Ltd. for " The Shell " from *Collected Poems*; and Mr. W. B. Yeats and Messrs. Macmillan & Co. Ltd. for " The Ballad of Father Gilligan " from *Collected Poems,* Vol. I.

E.W.P.

CONTENTS

BIRDS, BEASTS AND REPTILES

THINGS SEEN

CONTENTS

PEOPLE AND PLACES

COUNTRY FOLK AND THE COUNTRYSIDE

CONTENTS

SHIPS AND THE SEA

13

CONTENTS

MERRIMENT

JOURNEYS AND ENCOUNTERS

CONTENTS

CHRONOLOGICAL LIST OF AUTHORS

BIRDS, BEASTS AND REPTILES

THE PARROTS

Somewhere, somewhen I've seen,
But where or when I'll never know,
Three parrots of shrill green
With crests of shriller scarlet flying
Out of black cedars as the sun was dying
  Against cold peaks of snow.

From what forgotten life
Of other worlds I cannot tell
Flashes that screeching strife:
Yet the shrill colour and the strident crying
Sing through my blood and set my heart replying
  And jangling like a bell.

WILFRID WILSON GIBSON

THE BUZZARDS

When evening came and the warm glow grew deeper,
And every tree that bordered the green meadows
And in the yellow cornfields every reaper
And every corn-shock[1] stood above their shadows

---

[1] A heap of sheaves.

Flung eastward from their feet in longer measure,
Serenely far there swam in the sunny height
A buzzard and his mate who took their pleasure
Swirling and poising idly in golden light.

On great pied motionless moth-wings borne along,
  So effortless and so strong,
Cutting each other's paths together they glided,
Then wheeled asunder till they soared divided
Two valleys' width (as though it were delight
To part like this, being sure they could unite
So swiftly in their empty, free dominion),
Curved headlong downward, towered up the sunny steep,
Then, with a sudden lift of the one great pinion,
Swung proudly to a curve, and from its height
Took half a mile of sunlight in one long sweep.

And we, so small on the swift immense hillside,
Stood tranced, until our souls arose uplifted
  On those far-sweeping, wide,
Strong curves of flight—swayed up and hugely drifted,
Were washed, made strong and beautiful in the tide
Of sun-bathed air. But far beneath, beholden
Through shining deeps of air, the fields were golden
And rosy burned the heather where cornfields ended.
And still those buzzards whirled, while light withdrew
Out of the vales and to surging slopes ascended,
Till the loftiest flaming summit died to blue.

MARTIN ARMSTRONG

MILK FOR THE CAT

When the tea is brought at five o'clock,
And all the neat curtains are drawn with care,
The little black cat with bright green eyes
Is suddenly purring there.

At first she pretends, having nothing to do,
She has come in merely to blink by the grate,
But, though tea may be late or the milk may
    be sour,
She is never late.

And presently her agate eyes
Take a soft large milky haze,
And her independent casual glance
Becomes a stiff, hard gaze.

Then she stamps her claws or lifts her ears,
Or twists her tail and begins to stir,
Till suddenly all her lithe body becomes
One breathing, trembling purr.

The children eat and wriggle and laugh;
The two old ladies stroke their silk:
But the cat is grown small and thin with desire,
Transformed to a creeping lust for milk.

The white saucer like some full moon descends
At last from the clouds of the table above;
She sighs and dreams and thrills and glows,
Transfigured with love.

She nestles over the shining rim,
Buries her chin in the creamy sea;
Her tail hangs loose; each drowsy paw
Is doubled under each bending knee.

A long dim ecstasy holds her life;
Her world is an infinite shapeless white,
Till her tongue has curled the last holy drop,
Then she sinks back into the night.

Draws and dips her body to heap
Her sleepy nerves in the great arm-chair,
Lies defeated and buried deep
Three or four hours unconscious there.

HAROLD MONRO

HORSES ON THE CAMARGUE[1]

In the grey wastes of dread,
The haunts of shattered gulls where nothing moves
But in a shroud of silence like the dead,
I heard a sudden harmony of hooves,
And, turning, saw afar
A hundred snowy horses unconfined,
The silver runaways of Neptune's car
Racing, spray-curled, like waves before the wind.
Sons of the Mistral,[2] fleet
As him with whose strong gusts they love to flee,
Who shod the flying thunders on their feet

[1] A marshy district in the south of France.
[2] A violent north-west wind.

20

And plumed them with the snortings of the sea;
Theirs is no earthly breed
Who only haunt the verges of the earth
And only on the sea's salt herbage feed—
Surely the great white breakers gave them birth.
For when for years a slave,
A horse of the Camargue, in alien lands,
Should catch some far-off fragrance of the wave
Carried far inland from his native sands,
Many have told the tale
Of how in fury, foaming at the rein,
He hurls his rider; and with lifted tail,
With coal-red eyes and cataracting mane,
Heading his course for home,
Though sixty foreign leagues before him sweep,
Will never rest until he breathes the foam
And hears the native thunder of the deep.
But when the great gusts rise
And lash their anger on these arid coasts,
When the scared gulls career with mournful cries
And whirl across the waste like driven ghosts:
When hail and fire converge,
The only souls to which they strike no pain
Are the white-crested fillies of the surge
And the white horses of the windy plain.
Then in their strength and pride
The stallions of the wilderness rejoice;
They feel their Master's trident in their side,
And high and shrill they answer to his voice.
With white tails smoking free,
Long streaming manes and arching necks, they show
Their kinship to their sisters of the sea—

And forward hurl their thunderbolts of snow.
Still out of hardship bred,
Spirits of power and beauty and delight
Have ever on such frugal pastures fed
And loved to course with tempests through the night.

ROY CAMPBELL

THE BULL

(From " The Seasons ")

Through all his lusty veins
The bull, deep-scorched, the raging passion feels.
Of pasture sick, and negligent of food,
Scarce seen he wades among the yellow broom,
While o'er his ample sides the rambling sprays
Luxuriant shoot; or through the mazy wood
Dejected wanders, nor the enticing bud
Crops, though it presses on his careless sense.
And oft, in jealous maddening fancy wrapt,
He seeks the fight; and, idly butting, feigns
His rival gored in every knotty trunk.
Him should he meet, the bellowing war begins:
Their eyes flash fury; to the hollowed earth,
Whence the sand flies, they mutter bloody deeds,
And, groaning deep, the impetuous battle mix:
While the fair heifer, balmy-breathing near,
Stands kindling up their rage. The trembling steed,
With this hot impulse seized in every nerve,
Nor heeds the rein, nor hears the sounding thong;
Blows are not felt; but, tossing high his head,

And by the well-known joy to distant plains
Attracted strong, all wild he bursts away;
O'er rocks, and woods, and craggy mountains flies;
And, neighing, on the aerial summit takes
The exciting gale; then, steep-descending, cleaves
The headlong torrents foaming down the hills,
Even where the madness of the straitened stream
Turns in black eddies round: such is the force
With which his frantic heart and sinews swell.

JAMES THOMSON

THE BELLS OF HEAVEN

'Twould ring the bells of Heaven
The wildest peal for years,
If Parson lost his senses
And people came to theirs,
And he and they together
Knelt down with angry prayers
For tamed and shabby tigers
And dancing dogs and bears,
And wretched, blind pit ponies,
And little hunted hares.

RALPH HODGSON

SNAKE

A snake came to my water-trough
On a hot, hot day, and I in pyjamas for the heat,
To drink there.

23

In the deep, strange-scented shade of the great dark
    carob-tree
I came down the steps with my pitcher
And must wait, must stand and wait, for there he was
    at the trough before me.

He reached down from a fissure in the earth-wall in
    the gloom
And trailed his yellow-brown slackness soft-bellied
    down, over the edge of the stone trough
And rested his throat upon the stone bottom,
And where the water had dripped from the tap, in a
    small clearness,
He sipped with his straight mouth,
Softly drank through his straight gums, into his slack
    long body,
Silently.

Someone was before me at my water-trough,
And I, like a second comer, waiting.

He lifted his head from his drinking, as cattle do,
And looked at me vaguely, as drinking cattle do,
And flickered his two-forked tongue from his lips, and
    mused a moment,
And stooped and drank a little more,
Being earth-brown, earth-golden from the burning,
    burning bowels of the earth
On the day of Sicilian July, with Etna smoking.

The voice of my education said to me
He must be killed,

For in Sicily the black, black snakes are innocent, the
    gold are venomous.
And voices in me said, If you were a man
You would take a stick and break him now, and finish
    him off.

But must I confess how I liked him,
How glad I was he had come like a guest in quiet, to
    drink at my water-trough
And depart peaceful, pacified, and thankless,
Into the burning bowels of this earth?

Was it cowardice, that I dared not kill him?
Was it perversity, that I longed to talk to him?
Was it humility, to feel so honoured?
I felt so honoured.

And yet those voices:
If you were not afraid, you would kill him!

And truly I was afraid, I was most afraid,
But even so, honoured still more
That he should seek my hospitality
From out the dark door of the secret earth.

He drank enough
And lifted his head, dreamily, as one who has drunken,
And flickered his tongue like a forked night on the air,
    so black,
Seeming to lick his lips,
And looked around like a god, unseeing, into the air,
And slowly turned his head,

And slowly, very slowly, as if thrice adream,
Proceeded to draw his slow length curving round
And climb again the broken bank of my wall-face.

And as he put his head into that dreadful hole,
And as he slowly drew up, snake-easing his shoulders,
and entered farther,
A sort of horror, a sort of protest against his with-
drawing into that horrid black hole,
Deliberately going into the blackness, and slowly draw-
ing himself after,
Overcame me now his back was turned.

I looked round, I put down my pitcher,
I picked up a clumsy log
And threw it at the water-trough with a clatter.

I think it did not hit him,
But suddenly that part of him that was left behind
convulsed in undignified haste,
Writhed like lightning, and was gone
Into the black hole, the earth-lipped fissure in the wall-
front,
At which, in the intense still noon, I stared with
fascination.

And immediately I regretted it.
I thought how paltry, how vulgar, what a mean act!
I despised myself and the voices of my accursed human
education.
And I thought of the albatross,[1]
And I wished he would come back, my snake.

[1] In Coleridge's " Ancient Mariner."

26

For he seemed to me again like a king,
Like a king in exile, uncrowned in the underworld,
Now due to be crowned again.

And so, I missed my chance with one of the lords
Of life.
And I have something to expiate;
A pettiness.

D. H. LAWRENCE

THINGS SEEN

THE EXPRESS

After the first powerful plain manifesto
The black statement of pistons, without more fuss
But gliding like a queen, she leaves the station.
Without bowing and with restrained unconcern
She passes the houses which humbly crowd outside,
The gasworks and at last the heavy page
Of death, printed by gravestones in the cemetery.
Beyond the town there lies the open country
Where, gathering speed, she acquires mystery,
The luminous self-possession of ships on ocean.
It is now she begins to sing—at first quite low,
Then loud, and at last with a jazzy madness—
The song of her whistle screaming at curves,
Of deafening tunnels, brakes, innumerable bolts.
And always light, aërial, underneath
Goes the elate[1] metre of her wheels.
Steaming through metal landscape on her lines
She plunges new eras of wild happiness
Where speed throws up strange shapes, broad curves
And parallels clean like the steel of guns.
At last, further than Edinburgh or Rome,
Beyond the crest of the world, she reaches night

[1] Triumphant rhythmical beat.

Where only a low streamline brightness
Of phosphorus on the tossing hills is white.
Ah, like a comet through flame she moves entranced
Wrapt in her music no bird song, no, nor bough
Breaking with honey buds, shall ever equal.

STEPHEN SPENDER

THE BRIDGE

Here, with one leap,
The bridge that spans the cutting; on its back
The load
Of the main road,
And under it the railway track.

Into the plains they sweep,
Into the solitary plains asleep,
The flowing lines, the parallel lines of steel—
Fringed with their narrow grass,
Into the plains they pass,
The flowing lines, like arms of mute appeal.

A cry
Prolonged across the earth—a call
To the remote horizons and the sky;
The whole east rushes down them with its light,
And the whole west receives them, with its pall
Of stars and night—
The flowing lines, the parallel lines of steel.

And with the fall
Of darkness, see! the red,

Bright anger of the signal, where it flares
Like a huge eye that stares
On some hid danger in the dark ahead.

A twang of wire—unseen
The signal drops; and, now instead
Of a red eye, a green.

Out of the silence grows
An iron thunder—grows, and roars, and sweeps,
Menacing!   The plain
Suddenly leaps,
Startled, from its repose—
Alert and listening. Now, from the gloom
Of the soft distance, loom
Three lights, and over them, a brush
Of tawny flame and flying spark—
Three pointed lights that rush,
Monstrous, upon the cringing dark.

And nearer, nearer, rolls the sound,
Louder the throb and roar of wheels,
The shout of speed, the shriek of steam;
The sloping bank,
Cut into flashing squares, gives back the clank
And grind of metal, while the ground
Shudders and the bridge reels—
As with a scream,
The train,
A rage of smoke, a laugh of fire,
A lighted anguish of desire,
A dream

Of gold and iron, of sound and flight,
Tumultuous roars across the night.

The train roars past—and, with a cry,
Drowned in a flying howl of wind,
Half-stifled in the smoke and blind,
The plain,
Shaken, exultant, unconfined,
Rises, flows on, and follows, and sweeps by,
Shrieking, to lose itself in distance and the sky.

JOHN REDWOOD ANDERSON

MORNING EXPRESS

Along the wind-swept platform, pinched and white,
The travellers stand in pools of wintry light,
Offering themselves to morn's long, slanting arrows.
The train's due; porters trundle laden barrows.
The train steams in, volleying resplendent clouds
Of sun-blown vapour. Hither and about,
Scared people hurry, storming the doors in crowds.
The officials seem to waken with a shout,
Resolved to hoist and plunder; some to the vans
Leap; others rumble the milk in gleaming cans.

Boys, indolent-eyed, from baskets leaning back,
Question each face; a man with a hammer steals
Stooping from coach to coach; with clang and clack,
Touches and tests, and listens to the wheels.
Guard sounds a warning whistle, points to the clock
With brandished flag, and on his folded flock

31

Claps the last door: the monster grunts: "Enough!"
Tightening his load of links with pant and puff.
Under the arch, then forth into blue day,
Glide the processional windows on their way,
And glimpse the stately folk who sit at ease
To view the world like kings taking the seas
In prosperous weather: drifting banners tell
Their progress to the counties; with them goes
The clamour of their journeying; while those
Who sped them stand to wave a last farewell.

SIEGFRIED SASSOON

THE CRANE

It stuns
The rapt attention, and it lifts
More than its load of many tons:
More than the turbine swung on high
So easily,
A toy
In its great grasp of steel.
It lifts my soul to feel
Joy in all human effort—joy
In its clear lines of loveliness;
For Beauty is the gesture of victorious Might,
And Strength exultant in success
Fashions the world's delight.
It shifts
More than the quarried cube of stone
From the fixed earth to the unfixèd sea:
It moves my very spirit, which had grown

One with the unmoving earth, and sets it free
On the free oceans where Adventure goes
Who knows
To what far glory? So, the old spell breaking,
Thought, from his deep enchantment waking,
Casts off the chains of what has been—regrets,
Fears, hesitations, doubts—and sets
Out on fresh voyage. And the crane
With its fast grapnels lays
Hold of my heart and lifts it up in praise—
Praise of the human hand
That made it, and the human brain
That planned.

A hundred feet, the tower
Rears its light frame of girder and tie;
And through its interlaced
Black lines
The blue June sky
In lozenge and triangle shines.
It stands foursquare,
Tenoned[1] in concrete, rooted in rock:
Rigid, efficient, spare:
The minimum of work and waste,
The maximum of power.
Iron ladders run
Steeply aloft—a stair
Climbing above the river and the town:
A sharp ascent into a purer air,
Into a clearer sun.
Far down

[1] Fitted in securely.

Between the girders, street and roof
Appear tilted; far off, a weather-cock,
As to some comrade like itself aloof
From the flat round of things,
Signals "Ahoy!" and flings
The flags of sunlight in a flash of signs.
It sees the first long-drawn
Streamer of smoke, ere round the distant river-bend
The steamer comes in sight;
It is the first to cry the dawn
"Good morrow!" and, at the day's end,
The first to see the first star's light.

Then, on the Atlas-shoulders of its strength
It bears the far-reached jib¹ out-swung:
An arm of abrupt metal flung
Full in the empty face of space;
An abrupt length
Of bridge stretched over an abyss
And leading nowhere; an immense
Menace of steel that, like some half-heard fate,
Sweeps round to dominate
Its wide circumference.
And on this highway, to and fro,
With steady movement slow
The cab
Crawls on its claw-like sprawl² of wheel;
While, like a hooded serpent with curved fangs,
The cable with its tackle hangs
And its twin hooks below.

¹ Long projecting arm.
² Array.

And it will grip and it will move
Now this, now that enormous weight,
With infinite precision—as if love
Had made its touch so delicate;
And it will lower, with the grace
Of absolute ease, huge stacks and great
Engines, and fit them into place
Not one sixteenth of a small inch amiss.

Under the jib the cab
Clings, as the nests of swallows cling
To the high eaves of houses. There, alone,
He sits, who is the soul
Of this vast body of steel;
And everything
In this vast body—chain,
Cable, and hook, and wheel,
Ratchet,[1] and brake, and the geared motors—feel
His calm, deliberate control.
His hand
Moves, and the giant structure thrills
Instant obedience to his will's
Command;
While from the cab, as from a brain
Nerves run to the least cell,
Wires,
Threading the attentive whole,
Flash to all parts, from that small citadel,
Inaudible mandates to make known
Mankind's desires.
For man, who is so weak a thing,

[1] Bar acting on teeth of cog-wheel.

Assumes thereby
Mighty extension and titanic force;
And in triumphant stature towers
Matched with the primal powers
Of Nature in sublime equality:
Thereby,
Godlike, he ordains the course
Of subject Destiny.

It stuns
The rapt attention, and it lifts
More than its load of many tons.
It lifts the blocks of Circumstance
Hewn in the quarried hills of Chance,
Wherewith to fling across the deep
Of chaos the rebellious, steep
And perilous causeway of the world's advance.
It lifts the engineries
By which man's far adventures steam,
Like ships, upon the seas
Of fabulous sunset and moon-bewildered dream.
It lifts the guns
Of his armed Science, by whose might
He holds at bay the invading fleets of pain,
And to the plain
Levels the fortresses of Night.
It lifts one step, one step, above
Their dangerous and heroic place,
The faith, the hope, the fortitude, the love
And tragic splendour of the human race.

JOHN REDWOOD ANDERSON

CHOOSING A MAST

This mast, new-shaved, through whom I rive[1] the ropes,
Says she was once an oread[2] of the slopes,
Graceful and tall upon the rocky highlands,
A slender tree, as vertical as noon,
And her low voice was lovely as the silence
Through which a fountain whistles to the moon,
Who now of the white spray must take the veil
And, for her songs, the thunder of the sail.

I chose her for her fragrance, when the spring
With sweetest resins swelled her fourteenth ring
And with live amber welded her young thews:
I chose her for the glory of the Muse,
Smoother of forms, that her hard-knotted grain,
Grazed by the chisel, shaven by the plane,
Might from the steel as cool a burnish take
As from the bladed moon a windless lake.

I chose her for her eagerness of flight
Where she stood tiptoe on the rocky height
Lifted by her own perfume to the sun,
While through her rustling plumes with eager sound
Her eagle spirit, with the gale at one,
Spreading wide pinions, would have spurned the
    ground
And her own sleeping shadow, had they not
With thymy fragrance charmed her to the spot.

[1] To drive through.
[2] Mountain nymph.

37

Lover of song, I chose this mountain pine
Not only for the straightness of her spine,
But for her songs: for there she loved to sing
Through a long noon's repose of wave and wing—
The fluvial swirling of her scented hair
Sole rill of song in all that windless air,
And her slim form the naiad[1] of the stream
Afloat upon the languor of its theme;

And for the soldier's fare on which she fed:
Her wine the azure, and the snow her bread;
And for her stormy watches on the height—
For only out of solitude or strife
Are born the sons of valour and delight;
And lastly for her rich exulting life
That with the wind stopped not its singing breath
But carolled on, the louder for its death.

Under a pine, when summer days were deep,
We loved the most to lie in love or sleep:
And when in long hexameters the west
Rolled his grey surge, the forest for his lyre,
It was the pines that sang us to our rest,
Loud in the wind and fragrant in the fire,
With legioned voices swelling all night long,
From Pelion[2] to Provence, their storm of song.

It was the pines that fanned us in the heat,
The pines, that cheered us in the time of sleet,
For which sweet gifts I set one dryad[3] free—

[1] Water nymph.
[2] A mountain in Greece.
[3] A nymph of the woods.

38

No longer to the wind a rooted foe,
This nymph shall wander where she longs to be
And with the blue north wind arise and go,
A silver huntress with the moon to run
And fly through rainbows with the rising sun;

And when to pasture in the glittering shoals
The guardian mistral drives his thundering foals,
And when like Tartar horsemen racing free
We ride the snorting fillies of the sea,
My pine shall be the archer of the gale
While on the bending willow curves the sail
From whose great bow the long keel shooting home
Shall fly, the feathered arrow of the foam.

ROY CAMPBELL

HANDS

Tempest without; within, the mellow glow
Of mingling lamp and firelight over all—
Etchings and water-colours on the wall,
Cushions and curtains of clear indigo,
Rugs damask-red and blue as Tyrian seas,
Deep chairs, black oaken settles, hammered brass,
Translucent porcelain and sea-green glass—
Colour and warmth and light and dreamy ease;

And I sit wondering where are now the hands
That wrought at anvil, easel, wheel, and loom—
Hands, slender, swart, red, gnarled—in foreign lands
Or English shops to furnish this seemly room;

And all the while, without, the windy rain
Drums like dead fingers tapping at the pane.

WILFRID WILSON GIBSON

ON FIRST LOOKING INTO CHAPMAN'S HOMER[1]

Much have I travell'd in the realms of gold,
   And many goodly states and kingdoms seen;
   Round many western islands have I been
Which bards in fealty to Apollo hold.

Oft of one wide expanse had I been told
   That deep-browed Homer rul'd as his demesne;
   Yet did I never breathe its pure serene
Till I heard Chapman speak out loud and bold:

Then felt I like some watcher of the skies
   When a new planet swims into his ken;
Or like stout Cortez, when with eagle eyes

He stared at the Pacific—and all his men
   Looked at each other with a wild surmise—
Silent, upon a peak in Darien.[2]

JOHN KEATS

[1] The poet had no knowledge of Greek. He first read Chapman's
translation at the age of twenty-one.
[2] Isthmus of Panama.

PEOPLE AND PLACES

THE LITTLE DANCERS

Lonely, save for a few faint stars, the sky
Dreams; and lonely, below, the little street
Into its gloom retires, secluded and shy.
Scarcely the dumb roar enters this soft retreat;
And all is dark, save where come flooding rays
From a tavern-window: there, to the brisk measure
Of an organ that down in an alley merrily plays,
Two children, all alone and no one by,
Holding their tattered frocks, thro' an airy maze
Of motion, lightly threaded with nimble feet,
Dance sedately: face to face they gaze,
Their eyes shining, grave with a perfect pleasure.

LAURENCE BINYON

THE BALLAD OF FATHER GILLIGAN

The old priest, Peter Gilligan,
   Was weary night and day,
For half his flock were in their beds,
   Or under green sods lay.

Once, while he nodded on a chair,
　　At the moth[1] hour of eve,
Another poor man sent for him,
　　And he began to grieve.

"I have no rest, nor joy, nor peace,
　　For people die and die ";
And after, cried he, " God forgive!
　　My body spake, not I! "

He knelt, and leaning on the chair,
　　He prayed and fell asleep;
And the moth hour went from the fields,
　　And stars began to peep.

They slowly into millions grew,
　　And leaves shook in the wind;
And God covered the world with shade,
　　And whispered to mankind.

Upon the time of sparrow chirp,
　　When the moths came once more,
The old priest Peter Gilligan
　　Stood upright on the floor.

" Mavrone, Mavrone![2] the man has died
　　While I slept on the chair ";
He roused his horse out of its sleep
　　And rode with little care.

He rode now as he never rode,
　　By rocky lane and fen;

[1] Twilight.
[2] Little mother (The Virgin Mary).

42

The sick man's wife opened the door:
  "Father! you come again!"

"And is the poor man dead?" he cried,
  "He died an hour ago."
The old Priest Peter Gilligan
  In grief swayed to and fro.

"When you were gone, he turned and died
  As merry as a bird."
The old priest Peter Gilligan
  He knelt him at that word.

"He who hath made the night of stars,
  For souls, who tire and bleed,
Sent one of His great angels down
  To help me in my need.

"He who is wrapped in purple robes,
  With planets in His care,
Had pity on the least of things
  Asleep upon a chair."

WILLIAM BUTLER YEATS

MISS THOMPSON GOES SHOPPING

In her lone cottage on the downs,   *Miss Thompson at Home.*
With winds and blizzards and great crowns
Of shining cloud, with wheeling plover
And short grass sweet with the small white
    clover,

Miss Thompson lived, correct and meek,
A lonely spinster, and every week
On market-day she used to go
Into the little town below,
Tucked in the great downs' hollow bowl
Like pebbles gathered in a shoal.

She goes a-
Marketing.

So, having washed her plates and cup
And banked the kitchen-fire up,
Miss Thompson slipped upstairs and dressed,
Put on her black (her second best),
The bonnet trimmed with rusty plush,
Peeped in the glass with simpering blush,
From camphor-smelling cupboard took
Her thicker jacket off the hook
Because the day might turn to cold.
Then, ready, slipped downstairs and rolled
The hearthrug back: then searched about,
Found her basket, ventured out,
Snecked the door and paused to lock it
And plunge the key in some deep pocket.
Then as she tripped demurely down
The steep descent, the little town
Spread wider till its sprawling street
Enclosed her and her footfalls beat
On hard stone pavement; and she felt
Those throbbing ecstasies that melt
Through heart and mind, as, happy, free,
Her small, prim personality
Merged into the seething strife
Of auction-marts and city life.

44

She visits the Bootmaker.

Serenely down the busy stream
Miss Thompson floated in a dream.
Now, hovering bee-like, she would stop
Entranced before some tempting shop,
Getting in people's way and prying
At things she never thought of buying:
Now wafted on without an aim:
Until in course of time she came
To Watson's bootshop. Long she pries
At boots and shoes of every size,
Brown football-boots, with bar and stud,
For boys that scuffle in the mud,
And dancing-pumps with pointed toes
Glassy as jet, and dull black bows;
Slim ladies' shoes with two-inch heel
And sprinkled beads of gold and steel—
" How anyone can wear such things! "
On either side the doorway springs
(As in a tropic jungle loom
Masses of strange thick-petalled bloom
And fruits misshapen) fold on fold
A growth of sandshoes rubber-soled,
Clambering the door-posts, branching, spawn-
     ing,
Their barbarous bunches like an awning
Over the windows and the doors.
But, framed among the other stores,
Something has caught Miss Thompson's eye
(O worldliness!   O vanity!),
A pair of slippers—scarlet plush.
Miss Thompson feels a conscious blush
Suffuse her face, as though her thought

45

Had ventured further than it ought.
But O that colour's rapturous singing
And the answer in her lone heart ringing!
She turns (O Guardian Angels stop her
From doing anything improper!),
She turns; and see, she stoops and bungles
In through the sandshoes' hanging jungles,
Away from light and common sense,
Into the shop dim-lit and dense
With smells of polish and tanned hide.

Mrs. Watson.

Soon from a dark recess inside,
Fat Mrs. Watson comes slip-slop
To mind the business of the shop.
She walks flat-footed with a roll—
A serviceable, homely soul,
With kindly, ugly face like dough,
Hair dull and colourless as tow.
A huge Scotch-pebble fills the space
Between her bosom and her face.
One sees her making beds all day.
Miss Thompson let her say her say
" So chilly for the time of year.
It's ages since we saw you here."
Then, heart a-flutter, speech precise,
Describes the shoes and asks the price.
"Them, Miss? Ah, them is six-and-nine."
Miss Thompson shudders down the spine.
(Dream of impossible romance).
She eyes them with a wistful glance,

Wrestles with
a Temptation;

Torn between good and evil. Yes,
For half-a-minute and no less

Miss Thompson strives with seven devils,
Then, soaring over earthly levels,
Turns from the shoes with lingering touch—
" Ah, six-and-nine is far too much. And is Saved.
Sorry to trouble you. Good day! "

A little farther down the way She visits the
Fishmonger,
Stands Miles's fish-shop, whence is shed
So strong a smell of fishes dead
That people of a subtler sense
Hold their breath and hurry thence.
Miss Thompson hovers there and gazes:
Her housewife's knowing eye appraises
Salt and fresh, severely cons
Kippers bright as tarnished bronze;
Great cods disposed upon the sill
Chilly and wet, with gaping gill,
Flat head, glazed eye, and mute, uncouth,
Shapeless, wan, old-woman's mouth.
Next, a row of soles and plaice
With querulous and twisted face,
And red-eyed bloaters, golden-grey;
Smoked haddocks ranked in neat array;
A group of smelts that take the light
Like slips of rainbow, pearly bright;
Silver trout with rosy spots,
And coral shrimps with keen black dots
For eyes, and hard and jointed sheath
And crisp tails curving underneath.
But there upon the sanded floor,
More wonderful in all that store
Than anything on slab or shelf,

47

Mr. Miles.

Stood Miles, the fishmonger, himself.
Foursquare he stood and filled the place.
His huge hands and his jolly face
Were red. He had a mouth to quaff
Pint after pint; a sounding laugh,
But wheezy at the end, and oft
His eyes bulged outwards and he coughed.
Aproned he stood from chin to toe.
The apron's vertical long flow
Warped grandly outwards to display
His hale, round belly hung midway,
Whose apex was securely bound
With apron-strings wrapped round and round.
Outside, Miss Thompson, small and staid,
Felt, as she always felt, afraid
Of this huge man who laughed so loud
And drew the notice of the crowd.
Awhile she paused in timid thought,
Then promptly hurried in and bought
" Two kippers, please. Yes, lovely weather."
" Two kippers? Sixpence altogether ":
And in her basket laid the pair
Wrapped face to face in newspaper.

Relapses into
Temptation;

Then on she went, as one half blind,
For things were stirring in her mind:
Then turned about with fixed intent
And, heading for the bootshop, went

And Falls.

Straight in and bought the scarlet slippers,
And popped them in beside the kippers.

She visits the
Chemist,

So much for that. From there she tacked,
Still flushed by this decisive act,

48

Westward, and came without a stop
To Mr. Wren the chemist's shop,
And stood awhile outside to see
The tall big-bellied bottles three—
Red, blue, and emerald, richly bright
Each with its burning core of light.
The bell chimed as she pushed the door.
Spotless the oilcloth on the floor,
Limpid as water each glass case,
Each thing precisely in its place.
Rows of small drawers, black-lettered each
With curious words of foreign speech,
Rose high above the other ware.
The old strange fragrance filled the air,
A fragrance like the garden pink,
But tinged with vague medicinal stink
Of camphor, soap, new sponges, blent
With chloroform and violet scent.

And Wren the Chemist, tall and spare   Mr. Wren.
Stood gaunt behind his counter there.
Quiet and very wise he seemed,
With skull-like face, bald head that gleamed:
Through spectacles his eyes looked kind.
He wore a pencil tucked behind
His ear.   And never he mistakes
The wildest signs the doctor makes
Prescribing drugs.   Brown paper, string,
He will not use for any thing,
But all in neat white parcels packs
And sticks them up with sealing-wax.
Miss Thompson bowed and blushed, and then

Undoubting bought of Mr. Wren,
Being free from modern scepticism,
A bottle for her rheumatism:
Also some peppermints to take
In case of wind; an oval cake
Of scented soap; a penny square
Of pungent naphthaline to scare
The moth. And after Wren had wrapped
And sealed the lot, Miss Thompson clapped
Them in beside the fish and shoes:
" Good day," she says, and off she goes.

Is led away by
the Pleasures of
the Town,

Beelike Miss Thompson, whither next?
Outside, you pause awhile, perplext,
Your bearings lost. Then all comes back
And round she wheels, hot on the track

Such as
Groceries and
Millinery,

Of Giles the Grocer: and from there
To Emilie the Milliner,
There to be tempted by the sight
Of hats and blouses fiercely bright.
(O guard Miss Thompson, Powers that Be,
From Crudeness and Vulgarity.)

And Other
Allurements;

Still on from shop to shop she goes
With sharp bird's-eye, inquiring nose,
Prying and peering, entering some,
Oblivious of the thought of home.
The town brimmed up with deep-blue haze,
But still she stayed to flit and gaze,
Her eyes ablur with rapturous sights,
Her small soul full of small delights,
Empty her purse, her basket filled.

The traffic in the town was stilled.
The clock struck six. Men thronged the
    inns.
Dear, dear, she should be home long since.

But at length is
Convinced of
Indiscretion,

Then as she climbed the misty downs,
The lamps were lighted in the town's
Small streets. She saw them star by star
Multiplying from afar:
Till, mapped beneath her, she could trace
Each street, and the wide square market-
    place
Sunk deeper and deeper as she went
Higher up the steep ascent.
And all that soul-uplifting stir
Step by step fell back from her,
The glory gone, the blossoming
Shrivelled, and she, a small, frail thing,
Carrying her laden basket. Till
Darkness and silence of the hill
Received her in their restful care
And stars came dropping through the air.

And returns
home.

But loudly, sweetly sang the slippers
In the basket with the kippers;
And loud and sweet the answering thrills
From her lone heart on the hills.

                MARTIN ARMSTRONG

THE VILLAGE SCHOOLMASTER

(From " The Deserted Village ")

Beside yon straggling fence that skirts the way,
With blossomed furze unprofitably gay,
There, in his noisy mansion, skilled to rule,
The village master taught his little school;
A man severe he was, and stern to view;
I knew him well, and every truant knew;
Well had the boding tremblers learned to trace
The day's disasters in his morning face;
Full well they laughed with counterfeited glee
At all his jokes, for many a joke had he;
Full well the busy whisper, circling round,
Conveyed the dismal tidings when he frowned:
Yet he was kind; or if severe in aught,
The love he bore to learning was in fault.
The village all declared how much he knew;
'Twas certain he could write and cypher too;
Lands he could measure, terms and tides presage,
And e'en the story ran that he could gauge.
In arguing, too, the parson owned his skill,
For e'en though vanquished, he could argue still;
While words of learned length and thund'ring sound
Amazed the gazing rustics ranged around,
And still they gazed, and still the wonder grew
That one small head could carry all he knew.
But past is all his fame. The very spot,
Where many a time he triumphed, is forgot.

OLIVER GOLDSMITH

A CINQUE PORT

Below the down the stranded town,
  What may betide forlornly waits,
With memories of smoky skies,
  When Gallic navies crossed the straits;
When waves with fire and blood grew bright,
And cannon thundered through the night.

With swinging stride the rhythmic tide
  Bore to the harbour barque and sloop;
Across the bar the ship of war,
  In castled stern and lanterned poop,
Came up with conquests on her lee,
The stately mistress of the sea.

Where argosies have wooed the breeze,
  The simple sheep are feeding now;
And near and far across the bar
  The ploughman whistles at the plough;
Where once the long waves washed the shore,
Larks from their lowly lodgings soar.

Below the down the stranded town
  Hears far away the rollers beat;
About the wall the seabirds call;
  The salt wind murmurs through the street;
Forlorn the sea's forsaken bride
Awaits the end that shall betide.

JOHN DAVIDSON

IN LADY STREET

All day long the traffic goes
In Lady Street by dingy rows
Of sloven houses, tattered shops—
Fried fish, old clothes and fortune-tellers—
Tall trams on silver-shining rails,
With grinding wheels and swaying tops,
And lorries with their corded bales,
And screeching cars. "Buy, buy!" the
    sellers
Of rags and bones and sickening meat
Cry all day long in Lady Street.

And when the sunshine has its way
In Lady Street, then all the grey
Dull desolation grows in state
More dull and grey and desolate,
And the sun is a shamefast thing,
A lord not comely-housed, a god
Seeing what gods must blush to see,
A song where it is ill to sing,
And each gold ray despiteously
Lies like a gold ironic rod.

Yet one grey man in Lady Street
Looks for the sun. He never bent
Life to his will, his travelling feet
Have scaled no cloudy continent,
Nor has the sickle-hand been strong.
He lives in Lady Street; a bed,
Four cobwebbed walls.

54

But all day long
A time is singing in his head
Of youth in Gloucester lanes. He hears
The wind among the barley blades,
The tapping of the woodpeckers
On the smooth beeches, thistle-spades
Slicing the sinewy roots; he sees
The hooded filberts in the copse
Beyond the loaded orchard trees,
The netted avenues of hops;
He smells the honeysuckle thrown
Along the hedge. He lives alone,
Alone—yet not alone, for sweet
Are Gloucester lanes in Lady Street.

Aye, Gloucester lanes. For down below
The cobwebbed room this grey man plies
A trade, a coloured trade. A show
Of many-coloured merchandise
Is in his shop. Brown filberts there,
And apples red with Gloucester air,
And cauliflowers he keeps, and round
Smooth marrows grown on Gloucester
    ground,
Fat cabbages and yellow plums,
And gaudy brave chrysanthemums;
And times a glossy pheasant lies
Among his store, not Tyrian dyes
More rich than are the neck-feathers;
And times a prize of violets,
Or dewy mushrooms satin-skinned,
And times an unfamiliar wind

Robbed of its woodland favour stirs
Gay daffodils this grey man sets
Among his treasure.

All day long
In Lady Street the traffic goes
By dingy houses, desolate rows
Of shops that stare like hopeless eyes.
Day long the sellers cry their cries,
The fortune-tellers tell no wrong
Of lives that know not any right,
And drift, that has not even the will
To drift, toils through the day until
The wage of sleep is won at night.
But this grey man heeds not at all
The hell of Lady Street. His stall
Of many-coloured merchandise
He makes a shining paradise,
As all day long chrysanthemums
He sells, and red and yellow plums
And cauliflowers. In that one spot
Of Lady Street the sun is not
Ashamed to shine and send a rare
Shower of colour through the air;
The grey man says the sun is sweet
On Gloucester lanes in Lady Street.

JOHN DRINKWATER

56

EDGAR'S DESCRIPTION OF DOVER CLIFF

(From " King Lear " IV. vi)

How fearful
And dizzy 'tis to cast one's eyes so low!
And crows and choughs that wing the midway air
Show scarce so gross as beetles: half-way down
Hangs one that gathers samphire, dreadful trade!
Methinks he seems no bigger than his head:
The fishermen that walk upon the beach
Appear like mice; and yond tall anchoring bark
Diminish'd to her cock, her cock, a buoy
Almost too small for sight: the murmuring surge,
That on the unnumber'd idle pebbles chafes,
Cannot be heard so high. I'll look no more,
Lest my brain turn, and the deficient sight
Topple down headlong.

WILLIAM SHAKESPEARE

LONDON

(From " The Prelude ")

Rise up, thou monstrous ant-hill[1] on the plain
Of a too busy world! Before me flow,
Thou endless stream of men and moving things!
Thy every-day appearance, as it strikes—
With wonder heightened, or sublimed by awe—
On strangers, of all ages; the quick dance

---

[1] Cobbett in his " Rural Rides " called London a wen.

Of colours, lights, and forms; the deafening din;
The comers and the goers face to face,
Face after face; the string of dazzling wares,
Shop after shop, with symbols, blazoned names,
And all the tradesman's honours overhead:
Here, fronts of houses, like a title-page
With letters huge inscribed from top to toe;
Stationed above the door, like guardian saints;
There, allegoric shapes, female or male,
Or physiognomies of real men,
Land-warriors, kings, or admirals of the sea,
Boyle, Shakespeare, Newton, or the attractive head
Of some quack-doctor, famous in his day.

Meanwhile the roar continues, till at length,
Escaped as from an enemy, we turn
Abruptly into some sequestered nook,
Still as a sheltered place when winds blow loud!

WILLIAM WORDSWORTH

COUNTRY FOLK AND THE COUNTRYSIDE

MOLE-CATCHER

With coat like any mole's, as soft and black,
And hazel bows bundled beneath his arm,
With long-helved spade and rush bag on his back,
The trapper plods alone about the farm:
And spies new mounds in the ripe pasture-land,
And where the lob-worms writhe up in alarm
And easy sinks the spade, he takes his stand
Knowing the moles' dark highroad runs below:
Then sharp and square he chops the turf, and day
Gloats on the opened turnpike through the clay.
Out from his wallet hurry pin and prong,
And trap, and noose to tie it to the bow;
And then his grand arcanum,[1] oily and strong,
Found out by his forefather years ago
To scent the peg and witch the moles along.
The bow is earthed and arched ready to shoot
And snatch the death-knot fast round the first mole
Who comes and snuffs well pleased and tries to root
Past the sly nose peg; back again is put

[1] A secret.

The mould, and death left smirking in the hole.
The old man goes and tallies all his snares
And finds the prisoners there and takes his toll.

And moles to him are only moles; but hares
See him afield and scarcely cease to nip
Their dinners, for he harms not them; he spares
The drowning fly that of his ale would sip
And throws the ant the crumbs of comradeship.
And every time he comes into his yard
Grey linnet knows he brings the groundsel sheaf,
And clatters round the cage to be unbarred,
And on his finger whistles twice as hard.—
What his old vicar says, is his belief,
In the side pew he sits and hears the truth;
And never misses once to ring his bell
On Sundays night and morn, nor once since youth
Has heard the chimes afield, but has heard tell
There's not a peal in England sounds so well.

EDMUND BLUNDEN

FARMER'S BOY[1]

He waits all day beside his little flock
And asks the passing stranger what 's o'clock,
But those who often pass his daily tasks
Look at their watch and tell before he asks.
He mutters stories to himself and lies
Where the thick hedge the warmest house supplies,

[1] The poet was the son of a Northamptonshire labourer and he
was himself at one time a herd boy.

And when he hears the hunters far and wide
He climbs the highest tree to see them ride—
He climbs till all the fields are bleak and bare
And makes the old crow's nest an easy chair.
And soon his sheep are got in other grounds—
He hastens down and fears his master come.
He stops the gap and keeps them all in bounds
And tends them closely till it 's time for home.

JOHN CLARE.

THE THIRD PASTOR'S SONG

Who can live in heart so glad
As the merry country lad?
Who upon a fair green balk
May at pleasure sit and walk,
And amid the azure skies
See the morning sun arise,—
While he hears in every spring
How the birds do chirp and sing;
Or, before the hounds in cry,
See the hare go stealing by;
Or, along the shallow brook,
Angling with a baited hook,
See the fishes leap and play
In a blessed sunny day;
Or to hear the partridge call,
Till she have her covey all;
Or to see the subtle fox,
How the villain plies the box;
After feeding on his prey,
How he closely sneaks away,

61

Through the hedge and down the furrow,
Till he gets into his burrow;
Then the bee to gather honey,
And the little black-haired coney
On a bank for sunny place
With her forefeet wash her face:
Are not these, with thousands moe
Than the courts of kings do know,
The true pleasing spirit's sights,
That may breed true love's delights?
But with all this happiness,
To behold that shepherdess,
To whose eyes all shepherds yield
All the fairest of the field,
Fair Aglaia,[1] in whose face,
Lives the shepherd's highest grace;
In whose worthy wonder's praise
See what her true shepherd says.
She is neither proud nor fine,
But in spirit more divine;
She can neither lour nor leer,
But a sweeter smiling cheer;
She had never painted face,
But a sweeter smiling grace;
She can never love dissemble,
Truth doth so her thoughts assemble,
That, where wisdom guides her will,
She is kind and constant still.
All in sum, she is that creature
Of that truest comfort's nature
That doth show (but in exceedings)

[1] The name of one of the three Graces.

How their praises had their breedings.
Let then poets fain their pleasure,
In their fictions of love's treasure;
Proud high spirits seek their graces,
In their idol painted faces;
My love's spirit's lowliness,
In affection's humbleness,
Under heaven no happiness
Seeks, but in this shepherdess.
For whose sake I say and swear,
By the passions that I bear,
Had I got a kingly grace,
I would leave my kingly place,
And in heart be truly glad
To become a country lad;
Hard to lie, and go full bare,
And to feed on hungry fare;
So I might but live to be,
Where I might but sit to see,
Once a day, or all day long,
The sweet subject of my song;
In Aglaia's only eyes
All my worldly Paradise.

NICHOLAS BRETON

THE THATCHER

(From " The Land ")

Thatcher with carpet bound about his knees
Tramps farm to farm with slow deliberate stride.
Thatchers are rare, these days, he'd have you know,

Good thatchers, those that go
About their business as it were a pride,
Scorning Dutch[1] barns and mushrooms such as these,
New-fangled, driving out a settled trade.
Once there were thatchers, ah, could hip[2] a roof
Easy as twist a sheaf; were not afraid
Of any rain, since work was weather-proof.
East Anglia bred them, where the reeds grow grey
Mile upon fenny mile, and ducks go home
Over the level wastes of dyke and sluice.
Still maundering on, he sorts his pegs, his comb,
His wooden bat, his twine, in neat array,
Trimming his straw,—full length of wheaten straw,—
Watered and sweated ready to its use,
Sweet in the yelm,[3] for thatch without a flaw.
Grumbling and boasting turn and turn about,
Having told the tally of the needed threaves,[4]
He mounts his ladder, pocket full of splines,[5]
And packs his yelms, and calls his mate a lout
If he disturb one straw from ordered lines.
Proud of his stelch,[6] and prouder of his eaves,
Proud of his skill to thatch an awkward pent,
He is an artist with a long descent,
Brother to workers in peculiar crafts;
To the old wheel-wright, punctual timber-master,
—Could tell you whether wood were frow[7] or doted

[1] Framework of a barn to protect hay or straw.
[2] To shape the angle formed by the sides of a roof.
[3] Bundle of straw.
[4] A number of sheaves of straw.
[5] A narrow strip of wood.
[6] The angle of the slope of the thatched roof.
[7] Brittle or decayed.

Before the trunk was opened; often quoted
The Bible; could turn out a pair of shafts
With straight and proper grain; adzed every spoke
By hand, and never had one cracked or bent;—
Brother to pargetter,[1] with hair and plaster,
Combing the diaper[2] on porous lime,
Pleased as a child with patterns he'd invent;
Brother to all the slow fastidious folk
Whose care is matched by their disdain of time;
To basket-makers, shaping Kentish bodges;[3]
To osier-weavers, twisting supple wands,
To Jack-of-all-trades with his sundry dodges;
Brick-layer, even, carrying his hod;
To Down-bred shepherds, puddling secret ponds,
So jealous of their mystery, for dew;
Lastly, to dowser, forcing virgin wells,
That changeling of the willows, simple, odd,
Touched by some finger laid on him askew
At birth by nixie or by water-god;
But dowser[4] never knows, or never tells.
Smiling, the willow upright in his hold,
Vacant he lags across the thirsty miles;
Shall water pull him? or shall buried gold,
Panoply of a Dane, beneath a mound?
But dowser never knew, or never told.
Only, he pauses when he feels the switch
Quicken between his fingers, curtsey, twitch;
Pauses, and points, and smiles,
And loses interest; for water's found.

V. SACKVILLE-WEST

[1] Plasterer.   [3] Measure of oats.
[2] Pattern.   [4] Water diviner.

MARKET DAY

With arms and legs at work and gentle stroke
That urges switching tail nor mends his pace,
On an old ribbed and weather-beaten horse,
The farmer goes jog-trotting to the fair.
Both keep their pace that nothing can provoke
Followed by brindled dog that snuffs the ground
With urging bark and hurries at his heels,
His hat slouched down, and greatcoat buttoned close
Bellied like hooped keg, and chuffy[1] face
Red as the morning's sun, he takes his round
And talks of stock: and when his jobs are done
And Dobbin's hay is eaten from the rack,
He drinks success to corn in language hoarse,
And claps old Dobbin's hide, and potters back.

JOHN CLARE

[1] Surly looking.

THE WOODMAN AND HIS DOG
(*From " The Task "*[1])

Forth goes the woodman, leaving unconcern'd
The cheerful haunts of man, to wield the axe
And drive the wedge in yonder forest drear,
From morn to eve his solitary task.

[1] When the poet's friend, Lady Austen, suggested that he should make the sofa in his room the subject of his next poem, he set about the " task." It commences with the sofa, but Cowper soon turns to country scenes and describes them with great faithfulness.

Shaggy, and lean, and shrewd, with pointed ears
And tail cropp'd short, half lurcher, and half cur,
His dog attends him. Close behind his heel
Now creeps he slow; and now with many a frisk
Wide scampering, snatches up the drifted snow
With ivory teeth, or ploughs it with his snout;
Then shakes his powder'd coat, and barks for joy.
Heedless of all his pranks, the sturdy churl
Moves right toward the mark; nor stops for aught,
But now and then with pressure of his thumb
To adjust the fragrant charge of a short tube
That fumes beneath his nose: the trailing cloud
Streams far behind him, scenting all the air.

WILLIAM COWPER

THE IDLERS

The gipsies lit their fires by the chalk-pit gate anew,
And the hoppled horses supped in the further dusk and
dew;
The gnats flocked round the smoke like idlers as they
were
And through the gorse and bushes the owls began to
churr.

An ell above the woods the last of sunset glowed
With a dusky gold that filled the pond beside the road;
The cricketers had done, the leas all silent lay,
And the carrier's clattering wheels went past and died
away.

The gipsies lolled and gossiped, and ate their stolen
    swedes,
Made merry with mouth-organs, worked toys with piths
    of reeds:
The old wives puffed their pipes, nigh as black as their
    hair,
And not one of them all seemed to know the name of
    care.

EDMUND BLUNDEN

THE GIPSIES

(From " The Task ")

  I see a column of slow-rising smoke
O'ertop the lofty wood that skirts the wild.
A vagabond and useless tribe there eat
Their miserable meal. A kettle, slung
Between two poles upon a stick transverse,
Receives the morsel; flesh obscene of dog,
Or vermin, or, at best, of cock purloin'd
From his accustom'd perch. Hard-faring race!
They pick their fuel out of ev'ry hedge,
Which, kindled with dry leaves, just saves unquench'd
The spark of life. The sportive wind blows wide
Their flutt'ring rags, and shows a tawny skin,
The vellum of the pedigree they claim.
Great skill have they in palmistry, and more
To conjure clean away the gold they touch,
Conveying worthless dross into its place;
Loud when they beg, dumb only when they steal.

Strange that a creature rational, and cast
In human mould, should brutalize by choice
His nature, and, though capable of arts
By which the world might profit and himself,
Self-banish'd from society, prefer
Such squalid sloth to honourable toil!
Yet even these, though feigning sickness oft
They swathe the forehead, drag the limping limb,
And vex their flesh with artificial sores,
Can change their whine into a mirthful note
When safe occasion offers; and with dance,
And music of the bladder and the bag,
Beguile their woes, and make the woods resound.
Such health and gaiety of heart enjoy
The houseless rovers of the sylvan world;
And breathing wholesome air, and wand'ring much,
Need other physic none to heal th' effects
Of loathsome diet, penury, and cold.

WILLIAM COWPER

GIPSIES

The gipsies seek wide sheltering woods again,
With droves of horses flock to mark their lane,
And trample on dead leaves, and hear the sound,
And look and see the black clouds gather round,
And set their camps, and free from muck and mire,
And gather stolen sticks to make the fire.
The roasted hedgehog, bitter though as gall,
Is eaten up and relished by them all.

They know the woods and every fox's den
And get their living far away from men;
The shooters ask them where to find the game,
The rabbits know them and are almost tame.
The aged women, tawny with the smoke,
Go with the winds and crack the rotted oak.

JOHN CLARE

THE YEOMAN

(From " Canterbury Tales ")

A Yeman hadde he, and servaunts namo[1]
At that tyme, for him liste ryde so;
And he was clad in cote and hood of grene;
A sheef of pecok-arwes[2] brighte and kene
Under his belt he bar ful thriftily;
(Wel coude he dresse his takel[3] yemanly:
His arwes drouped noght with fetheres lowe),
And in his hand he bar a mighty bowe.
A not-heed[4] hadde he, with a broun visage.
Of wode-craft wel coude he al the usage.
Upon his arm he bar a gay bracer,[5]
And by his syde a swerd and a bokeler,
And on that other syde a gay daggere,
Harneised wel, and sharp as point of spere;
A Cristofre[6] on his brest of silver shene.

---

[1] No more.
[2] Arrows with peacock's feathers.
[3] Archery gear.
[4] Cropped head.
[5] A guard for the arm (archery).
[6] A small figure of St. Christopher.

An horn he bar, the bawdrik[1] was of grene;
A forster was he, soothly, as I gesse.

GEOFFREY CHAUCER

[1] Bandolier.

THE YEOMAN

(*From " The Land "*)

His heart is wider than his purse,
Take all in all; but narrower than each
The portals of his speech.
Few words must serve his turn,
For he's sagacious who lives taciturn,
And airs no noisy cunning of his trade,
But keeps his private purpose deeply laid;
Gives neighbours nothing of his confidence,
And takes his counsel of his own good sense.
No wise man utters what he inly knows;
Certainty in a loose uncertain world
Is far too firm a treasure; wiseman goes
Jealous and wary, keeping darkly furled
His small particular knowledge. So he plots
To get the better of his lands again;
Compels, coerces, sets in trim, allots,
Renews the old campaign.
His mind is but the map of his estate,
No broader than his acres, fenced and bound
Within the little England of his ground,
Squared neat between the hedgerows of his brain,
With here Lord's Meadow tilted on a hill,

And Scallops' Coppice ending in a gate,
And here the Eden passing by a mill,
And there the barn with thatch,
And here a patch of gorse, and there a patch
Of iris on the fringes of a pond,
And here Brook Orchard banded safe with grease;
All this he sees, and nothing sees beyond
The limits and the fealty of his lease.
Tenant of his inheritance,
Brief link in life's long circumstance,
One of the nameless, name-forgotten line
Descended from that nameless ancestor
Who cut a holding in the serried weald
Where droves of swine
Rootled for acorns underneath the oaks,
Anderida's[1] sole yield
When Drake played bowls at Plymouth, and the rare
Coach with the cumbrous spokes
Trundled along the single clay-wet track
To Sussex with drawn blinds, or journeyed back
To London on affairs of state, the fine
Heraldic blazon eloquent on the door;
Makers of land, one of the nameless line
That fenced, and tilled, and overcame the waste,
And cut the necessary gaps,
And shaped the fields, slow-paced,
Into their permanent design,
Each field with local name, not marked on maps,
How come by, how begotten,
Long since forgotten:

[1] An ancient British fortress on the site of Pevensey. The Weald
(Andredswold) was once a vast forest.

Clement's, the Roundabout, Black Mead and Bitter
    Docks,
Rough Shepherd, Horses' Houghs,
And trod the path that grew into this lane
Bending between the hedgerows, where
Convenience claimed a road,—for country road
Is natural growth, with here a curve
Skirting a tree felled long ago, a swerve
To let the rattling harrow pass, the wain
With trussed and swaying load
Lurch safely by, and empty pass again.

He tills the soil to-day,
Surly and grave, his difficult wage to earn.
Cities of discontent, the sickened nerve,
Are still a fashion that he will not learn.
His way is still the obstinate old way,
Even though his horses stare above the hedge,
And whinny, while the tractor drives its wedge
Where they were wont to serve,
And iron robs them of their privilege.
Still is his heart not given
To such encroachments on a natural creed;
Not wholly given, though he bows to need
By urgency and competition driven,
And vanity, to follow with the tide.
Still with a secret triumph he will say,
"Tractor for sand, maybe, but horse for clay,"
And in his calling takes a stubborn pride
That nature still defeats
The frowsty science of the cloistered men,
Their theory, their conceits;

The faith within him still derides the pen,
Experience his text-book. What have they,
The bookish townsmen in their dry retreats,
Known of December dawns, before the sun
Reddened the east, and fields were wet and grey?
When they have gone, another day begun,
By tracks into a quagmire trodden,
With sacks about their shoulders and the damp
Soaking until their very souls were sodden,
To help a sick beast, by a flickering lamp,
With rough words and kind hands?
Or felt their boots so heavy and so swere[1]
With trudging over cledgy[2] lands,
Held fast by earth, being to earth so near?

Book-learning they have known.
They meet together, talk, and grow most wise,
But they have lost, in losing solitude,
Something,—an inward grace, the seeing eyes,
The power of being alone;
The power of being alone with earth and skies,
Of going about a task with quietude,
Aware at once of earth's surrounding mood
And of an insect crawling on a stone.

V. SACKVILLE-WEST

[1] Heavy.   [2] Clayey.

MERRY MAID

Bonny and stout and brown, without a hat,
She frowns offended when they call her fat.

Yet fat she is, the merriest in the place,
And all can know she wears a pretty face.
But still she never heeds what praise can say,
But does the work, and oft runs out to play,
To run about the yard and ramp and noise,
And spring the mop upon the servant boys.
When old hens noise and cackle everywhere,
She hurries eager if the eggs are dear,
And runs to seek them when they lay away
To get them ready for the market day.
She gambols with the men and laughs aloud,
And only quarrels when they call her proud.

JOHN CLARE.

THE HOCK-CART[1]

Come, Sons of Summer, by whose toile
We are the Lords of Wine and Oile:
By whose tough labours, and rough hands,
We rip up first, then reap our lands.
Crown'd with the eares of corne, now come,
And, to the Pipe, sing Harvest home.
Come forth, my Lord, and see the Cart
Drest up with all the Country Art.
See, here a *Maukin*,[2] there a sheet,
As spotlesse pure, as it is sweet:
The Horses, Mares, and frisking Fillies,
(Clad, all, in Linnen, white as Lillies.)

[1] At Hock-tide there were many festive customs, including a Hock
Tuesday play and sports.
[2] Scarecrow or guy.

The Harvest Swaines, and Wenches bound
For joy, to see the *Hock-cart* crown'd.
About the Cart, heare how the Rout
Of Rurall Younglings raise the shout;
Pressing before, some coming after,
Those with a shout, and these with laughter.
Some blesse the Cart; some kisse the sheaves;
Some prank them up with Oaken leaves:
Some crosse the Fill-horse;[1] some with great
Devotion, stroak the home-borne wheat:
While other Rusticks, lesse attent
To Prayers than to Merryment,
Run after with their breeches rent.
Well, on, brave boys, to your Lord's Hearth,
Glitt'ring with fire; where, for your mirth,
Ye shall see first the large and cheefe
Foundation of your Feast, Fat Beefe:
With Upper Stories, Mutton, Veale
And Bacon (which makes full the meale),
With sev'rall dishes standing by,
As, here a Custard, there a Pie,
And here all tempting Frumentie.[2]
And for to make the merry cheere,
If smirking Wine be wanting here,
There's that, which drown all care, stout Beere;
Which freely drink to your Lord's health,
Then to the Plough (the Common-wealth),
Next to your Flailes, your Fanes, your Fatts;
Then to the Maids with Wheaten Hats:
To the rough Sickle, and crookt Scythe,

[1] The horse that goes between the shafts.
[2] A porridge made with wheat.

76

Drink, frollick, boyes, till all be blythe.
Feed, and grow fat; and as ye eat,
Be mindfull, that the lab'ring Neat
(As you) may have their fill of meat.
And know, besides, ye must revoke
The patient Oxe unto the Yoke,
And all goe back unto the Plough
And Harrow (though they're hang'd up now).
And, you must know, your Lord's word's true,
Feed him ye must, whose food fills you.
And that this pleasure is like raine,
Not sent ye for to drowne your paine,
But for to make it spring againe.

ROBERT HERRICK

THE WAGGONER

The old waggon drudges through the miry lane,
  By the skulking pond where the pollards frown,
Notched dumb surly images of pain;
  On a dulled earth the night droops down.

Wincing to slow and wistful airs
  The leaves on the shrubbed oaks know their hour,
And the unknown wandering spoiler bares
  The thorned black hedge of a mournful shower.

Small bodies fluster in the dead brown wrack
  As the stumbling shaft-horse jingles past
And the waggoner flicks his whip a crack;
  The odd light flares on shadows vast

Over the lodges and oasts[1] and byres[2]
   Of the darkened farm; the moment hangs wan
As though nature flagged and all desires.
   But in the dim court the ghost is gone

From the hug-secret yew to the penthouse wall
   And stooping there seems to listen to
The waggoner leading the grey to stall,
   As centuries past itself would do.

EDMUND BLUNDEN

A SPRING OF STORMS
(From " The Land ")

That was a spring of storms.   They prowled the night;
Low level lightning flickered in the east
Continuous.   The white pear-blossom gleamed
Motionless in the flashes; birds were still;
Darkness and silence knotted to suspense,
Riven by the premonitory glint
Of skulking storm, a giant that whirled a sword
Over the low horizon, and with tread
Earth-shaking ever threatened his approach,
But to delay his terror kept afar,
And held earth stayed in waiting like a beast
Bowed to receive a blow.   But when he strode
Down from his throne of hills upon the plain,
And broke his anger to a thousand shards
Over the prostrate fields, then leapt the earth,
Proud to accept his challenge; drank his rain;

[1] A kiln for drying malt or hops.
[2] A cow-shed.

Under his sudden wind tossed wild her trees;
Opened her secret bosom to his shafts;
The great drops spattered; then above the house
Crashed thunder, and the little wainscot shook
And the green garden in the lightning lay.

V. SACKVILLE-WEST

FAREWELL, REWARDS AND FAIRIES!

"Farewell, rewards and fairies!"
Good housewives now may say,
For now foul sluts in dairies
Do fare as well as they.
And though they sweep their hearths no less
Than maids were wont to do,
Yet who of late, for cleanliness,
Finds sixpence in her shoe?

At morning and at evening both,
You merry were and glad,
So little care of sleep or sloth
These pretty ladies had;
When Tom came home from labour,
Or Cis to milking rose,
Then merrily went their tabor,
And nimbly went their toes.

Witness those rings and roundelays
Of theirs, which yet remain,
Were footed in Queen Mary's days
On many a grassy plain;

But since of late, Elizabeth,
And later, James came in,
They never danced on any heath
As when the time hath been.

RICHARD CORBET

A MAY MORNING

In somer, when the shawes[1] be sheyne,[2]
  And leves be large and long,
Hit is full mery in feyre foreste
  To here the foulys song.

To see the dere draw to the dale
  And leve the hillés hee,
And shadow hem in the leves green,
  Under the grene-wode tree.

Hit befel on Whitsontide,
  Erly in a May mornyng,
The Sonne up faire can shyne,
  And the briddis mery can syng.

"This is a mery mornyng," seid Litulle John,
  "Be Hym that dyed on tree;
A more mery man than I am one
  Lyves not in Christianté.

"Pluk up thi hert, my dere mayster,"
  Litulle John can say,

---

[1] Thicket or copse.   [2] Bright.

" And thynk hit is a fulle fayre tyme
   In a mornynge of May."

ANONYMOUS

THE WAY THROUGH THE WOODS

They shut the road through the woods
    Seventy years ago.
Weather and rain have undone it again,
    And now you would never know
There was once a road through the woods
    Before they planted the trees.
It is underneath the coppice and heath,
    And the thin anemones.
    Only the keeper sees
That, where the ring-dove broods,
    And the badgers roll at ease,
There was once a road through the woods.

Yet, if you enter the woods
    Of a summer evening late,
When the night-air cools the trout-ringed pools
    Where the otter whistles his mate,
(They fear not men in the woods,
    Because they see so few.)
You will hear the beat of a horse's feet
    And the swish of a skirt in the dew,
    Steadily cantering through
The misty solitudes,
    As though they perfectly knew

The old lost road through the woods. . . .
But there is no road through the woods.

RUDYARD KIPLING

THE WOODS OF WESTERMAIN

Enter these enchanted woods,
    You who dare.
Nothing harms beneath the leaves
More than waves a swimmer cleaves.
Toss your heart up with the lark,
Foot at peace with mouse and worm,
    Fair you fare.
Only at a dread of dark
Quaver, and they quit their form:
Thousand eyeballs under hoods
    Have you by the hair.
Enter these enchanted woods,
    You who dare.

Here the snake across your path
Stretches in his golden bath:
Mossy-footed squirrels leap
Soft as winnowing plumes of Sleep:
Yaffles[1] on a chuckle skim
Low to laugh from branches dim:
Up the pine, where sits the star,
Rattles deep the moth-winged jar.
Each has business of his own;
But should you distrust a tone,

[1] Green wood-peckers.

Then beware.
Shudder all the haunted roods,
All the eyeballs under hoods
    Shroud you in their glare.
Enter these enchanted woods,
    You who dare.

GEORGE MEREDITH

NUTTING

    It seems a day
(I speak of one from many singled out)
One of those heavenly days that cannot die;
When, in the eagerness of boyish hope,
I left our cottage-threshold, sallying forth
With a huge wallet o'er my shoulders slung,
A nutting-crook in hand; and turned my steps
Tow'rd some far-distant wood, a Figure quaint,
Tricked out in proud disguise of cast-off weeds
Which for that service had been husbanded,
By exhortation of my frugal Dame—
Motley accoutrement, of power to smile
At thorns, and brakes, and brambles,—and in truth
More raggèd than need was! O'er pathless rocks,
Through beds of matted fern, and tangled thickets,
Forcing my way, I came to one dear nook
Unvisited, where not a broken bough
Drooped with its withered leaves, ungracious sign
Of devastation; but the hazels rose
Tall and erect, with tempting clusters hung,
A virgin scene!—A little while I stood,

Breathing with such suppression of the heart
As joy delights in; and with wise restraint
Voluptuous, fearless of a rival, eyed
The banquet;—or beneath the trees I sate
Among the flowers, and with the flowers I played;
A temper known to those who, after long
And weary expectation, have been blest
With sudden happiness beyond all hope.
Perhaps it was a bower beneath whose leaves
The violets of five seasons reappear
And fade, unseen by any human eye;
Where fairy water-breaks do murmur on
For ever; and I saw the sparkling foam,
And—with my cheek on one of those green stones
That, fleeced with moss, under the shady trees,
Lay round me, scattered like a flock of sheep—
I heard the murmur and the murmuring sound,
In that sweet mood when pleasure loves to pay
Tribute to ease; and, of its joy secure,
The heart luxuriates with indifferent things,
Wasting its kindliness on stocks and stones,
And on the vacant air. Then up I rose,
And dragged to earth both branch and bough, with
    crash
And merciless ravage: and the shady nook
Of hazels, and the green and mossy bower,
Deformed and sullied, patiently gave up
Their quiet being: and, unless I now
Confound my present feelings with the past;
Ere from the mutilated bower I turned
Exulting, rich beyond the wealth of kings,
I felt a sense of pain when I beheld

The silent trees, and saw the intruding sky.—
Then, dearest Maiden, move along these shades
In gentleness of heart; with gentle hand
Touch—for there is a spirit in the woods.

WILLIAM WORDSWORTH

TO A MOUNTAIN DAISY

On turning one down with the Plough, in April, 1786

Wee, modest, crimson-tippèd flow'r,
Thou's met me in an evil hour;
For I maun crush amang the stoure[1]
       Thy slender stem:
To spare thee now is past my pow'r,
       Thou bonnie gem.

Alas! it's no thy neibor sweet,
The bonnie lark, companion meet,
Bending thee 'mang the dewy weet
       Wi' spreckl'd breast,
When upward springing, blythe, to greet
       The purpling east.

Cauld blew the bitter-biting north
Upon thy early, humble birth;
Yet cheerfully thou glinted forth
       Amid the storm,
Scarce rear'd above the parent-earth
       Thy tender form.

[1] Dust

The flaunting flow'rs our gardens yield
High shelt'ring woods and wa's maun shield,
But thou, beneath the random bield[1]
      O' clod or stane,
Adorns the histie[2] stibble-field,
      Unseen, alane.

There, in thy scanty mantle clad,
Thy snawy bosom sun-ward spread,
Thou lifts thy unassuming head
      In humble guise;
But now the share uptears thy bed,
      And low thou lies!

ROBERT BURNS

[1] Shelter.   [2] Dry.

THE SILENT LAKE

(From " The Prelude ")

One summer evening (led by her) I found
A little boat tied to a willow tree
Within a rocky cave, its usual home.
Straight I unloosed her chain, and stepping in
Pushed from the shore. It was an act of stealth
And troubled pleasure, nor without the voice
Of mountain-echoes did my boat move on;
Leaving behind her still, on either side,

Small circles glittering idly in the moon,
Until they melted all into one track
Of sparkling light. But now, like one who rows,
Proud of his skill, to reach a chosen point
With an unswerving line, I fixed my view
Upon the summit of a craggy ridge,
The horizon's utmost boundary; far above
Was nothing but the stars and the grey sky.
She was an elfin pinnace; lustily
I dipped my oars into the silent lake,
And, as I rose upon the stroke, my boat
Went heaving through the water like a swan;
When, from behind that craggy steep till then
The horizon's bound, a huge peak, black and huge,
As if with voluntary power instinct
Upreared its head. I struck and struck again,
And growing still in stature the grim shape
Towered up between me and the stars, and still,
For so it seemed, with purpose of its own
And measured motion like a living thing,
Strode after me. With trembling oars I turned,
And through the silent water stole my way
Back to the covert of the willow tree;
There in her mooring-place I left my bark,—
And through the meadows homeward went, in grave
And serious mood; but after I had seen
That spectacle, for many days, my brain
Worked with a dim and undetermined sense
Of unknown modes of being; o'er my thoughts
There hung a darkness, call it solitude
Or blank desertion. No familiar shapes
Remained, no pleasant images of trees,

Of sea or sky, no colours of green fields;
But huge and mighty forms, that do not live,
Like living men, moved slowly through the mind
By day, and were a trouble to my dreams.

WILLIAM WORDSWORTH

SHIPS AND THE SEA

THE SHELL[1]

I

And then I pressed the shell
Close to my ear
And listened well.
And straightway, like a bell,
Came low and clear
The slow, sad murmur of far distant seas
Whipped by an icy breeze
Upon a shore
Wind-swept and desolate.
It was a sunless strand that never bore
The footprint of a man,
Nor felt the weight
Since time began
Of any human quality or stir,
Save what the dreary winds and waves incur.

II

And in the hush of waters was the sound
Of pebbles, rolling round,

[1] Compare with Tennyson's poem in " The Poets' Path."

89

For ever rolling, with a hollow sound;
And bubbling sea-weeds, as the waters go,
Swish to and fro
Their long, cold tentacles of slimy grey:
There was no day;
Nor ever came a night
Setting the stars alight
To wonder at the moon:
Was twilight only, and the frightened croon,
Smitten to whimpers, of the dreary wind
And waves that journeyed blind . .
And then I loosed my ear—oh, it was sweet
To hear a cart go jolting down the street.

JAMES STEPHENS

THE SEA

(From " Endymion ")

Far had he roam'd,

With nothing save the hollow vast, that foam'd
Above, around, and at his feet; save things
More dead than Morpheus'[1] imaginings:
Old rusted anchors, helmets, breastplates large
Of gone sea-warriors; brazen beaks and targe;
Rudders that for a hundred years had lost
The sway of human hand; gold vase emboss'd
With long-forgotten story, and wherein
No reveller had ever dipp'd a chin
But those of Saturn's vintage; mouldering scrolls,

---

[1] A god of dreams.

Writ in the tongue of heaven, by those souls
Who first were on the earth; and sculptures rude
In ponderous stone, developing the mood
Of ancient Nox;—then skeletons of man,
Of beast, behemoth, and leviathan,
And elephant, and eagle, and huge jaw
Of nameless monster. A cold leaden awe
These secrets struck into him; and unless
Dian had chased away that heaviness,
He might have died: but now, with cheered feel,
He onward kept; wooing these thoughts to steal
About the labyrinth in his soul of love.

JOHN KEATS

SAM

When Sam goes back in memory,
   It is to where the sea
Breaks on the shingle, emerald-green,
   In white foam, endlessly;
He says—with small brown eye on mine—
   "I used to keep awake,
And lean from my window in the moon,
   Watching those billows break.
And half a million tiny hands,
   And eyes, like sparks of frost,
Would dance and come tumbling into the moon,
   On every breaker tossed.
And all across from star to star,
   I've seen the watery sea,

With not a single ship in sight,
   Just ocean there, and me;
And heard my father snore. And once,
   As sure as I'm alive,
Out of those wallowing, moon-flecked waves
   I saw a mermaid dive;
Head and shoulders above the wave,
   Plain as I now see you,
Combing her hair, now back, now front,
   Her two eyes peeping through;
Calling me, ' Sam! '—quietlike—' Sam! ' . . .
   But me . . . I never went,
Making believe I kind of thought
   'Twas some one else she meant . . .
Wonderful lovely there she sat,
   Singing the night away,
All in the solitudinous sea
   Of that there lonely bay.
P'raps," and he'd smooth his hairless mouth,
   " P'raps if 'twere now, my son,
P'raps, if I heard a voice say, ' Sam! ' . . .
   Morning would find me gone."

                    WALTER DE LA MARE

THE SHIPMAN

(From " Canterbury Tales ")

A shipman was ther, woning[1] fer by weste:
For aught I woot, he was of Dertemouthe.
He rood up-on a rouncy,[2] as he couthe,

     [1] Dwelling.   [2] A nag.

In a gowne of falding[1] to the knee.
A daggere hanging on a laas hadde he
Aboute his nekke under his arm adoun.
The hote somer had maad his hewe al broun;
And, certeinly, he was a good felawe.
Ful many a draughte of wyn had he y-drawe
From Burdeux-ward, whyl that the chapman sleep.
Of nyce conscience took he no keep.
If that he faught, and hadde the hyer hond,
By water he sente hem hoom to every lond.
But of his craft to rekene wel his tydes,
His stremes and his daungers him bisydes,
His herberwe[2] and his mone, his lode-menage,[3]
Ther nas noon swich from Hulle to Cartage.
Hardy he was, and wys to undertake;
With many a tempest hadde his berd been shake.
He knew well alle the havenes, as they were,
From Gootlond[4] to the cape of Finistere,
And every cryke in Britayne and in Spayne;
His barge y-cleped[5] was the Maudelayne.
With us ther was a DOCTOUR OF PHISYK,
In al this world ne was ther noon him lyk.

GEOFFREY CHAUCER

[1] Cloth.   [2] Harbour.   [3] Pilotage.   [4] Jutland.   [5] Named.

THE LOTOS-EATERS[1]

" Courage! " he said, and pointed toward the land,
" This mounting wave will roll us shoreward soon."

[1] In " The Odyssey " Homer tells the story of the return of Odysseus from the siege of Troy. On the way he visited the land of the Lotos-Eaters who fed on the fruit of the Lotos. Those who ate this fruit lost all desire to return to their native land.

In the afternoon they came unto a land
In which it seemed always afternoon.
All round the coast the languid air did swoon,
Breathing like one that hath a weary dream.
Full-faced above the valley stood the moon;
And like a downward smoke, the slender stream
Along the cliff to fall and pause and fall did seem.

A land of streams! some, like a downward smoke,
Slow-dropping veils of thinnest lawn did go;
And some thro' wavering lights and shadows broke,
Rolling a slumbrous sheet of foam below.
They saw the gleaming river seaward flow
From the inner land: far off, three mountain-tops,
Three silent pinnacles of aged snow,
Stood sunset-flush'd: and, dew'd with showery drops,
Up-clomb the shadowy pine above the woven copse.

The charmed sunset linger'd low adown
In the red West: thro' mountain clefts the dale
Was seen far inland, and the yellow down
Border'd with palm, and many a winding vale
And meadow, set with slender galingale;[1]
A land where all things always seem'd the same!
And round about the keel with faces pale,
Dark faces pale against that rosy flame,
The mild-eyed melancholy Lotos-eaters came.

Branches they bore of that enchanted stem,
Laden with flower and fruit, whereof they gave
To each, but whoso did receive of them,

[1] A kind of sedge.

And taste, to him the gushing of the wave
Far far away did seem to mourn and rave
On alien shores; and if his fellow spake,
His voice was thin, as voices from the grave;
And deep-asleep he seem'd, yet all awake,
And music in his ears his beating heart did make.

They sat them down upon the yellow sand,
Between the sun and moon upon the shore;
And sweet it was to dream of Fatherland,
Of child, and wife, and slave; but evermore
Most weary seem'd the sea, weary the oar,
Weary the wandering fields of barren foam.
Then some one said, "We will return no more";
And all at once they sang, "Our island home
Is far beyond the wave; we will no longer roam."

LORD TENNYSON

ROUNDING CAPE HORN

(From " Dauber: A Poem "[1])

All through the windless night the clipper rolled
In a great swell with oily gradual heaves
Which rolled her down until her time-bells tolled,
Clang, and the weltering water moaned like beeves.
The thundering rattle of slatting[2] shook the sheaves,[3]

---

[1] John Masefield, the Poet Laureate, has probably based this poem on his own experiences, for like " Dauber " he ran away to sea early in life.
[2] The noise made by the sails.
[3] Pulleys.

Startles of water made the swing ports[1] gush,
The sea was moaning and sighing and saying "Hush!"

It was all black and starless. Peering down
Into the water, trying to pierce the gloom,
One saw a dim, smooth, oily glitter of brown
Heaving and dying away and leaving room
For yet another. Like the march of doom
Came those great powers of marching silences;
Then fog came down, dead-cold, and hid the seas.

They set the Dauber to the foghorn. There
He stood upon the poop, making to sound
Out of the pump the sailors' nasal blare,
Listening lest ice should make the note resound.
She bayed there like a solitary hound
Lost in a covert; all the watch she bayed.
The fog, come closelier down, no answer made.

Denser it grew, until the ship was lost.
The elemental hid her; she was merged
In mufflings of dark death, like a man's ghost,
New to the change of death, yet thither urged.
Then from the hidden waters something surged—
Mournful, despairing, great, greater than speech,
A noise like one slow wave on a still beach.

Mournful, and then again mournful, and still
Out of the night that mighty voice arose;
The Dauber at his foghorn felt the thrill.
Who rode that desolate sea? What forms were those?

[1] Iron doors in the side of the ship to let the water out.

Mournful, from things defeated, in the throes
Of memory of some conquered hunting-ground,
Out of the night of death arose the sound.

"Whales!" said the mate. They stayed there all night
    long
Answering the horn. Out of the night they spoke,
Defeated creatures who had suffered wrong,
But were still noble underneath the stroke.
They filled the darkness when the Dauber woke;
The men came peering to the rail to hear,
And the sea sighed, and the fog rose up sheer.

A wall of nothing at the world's last edge,
Where no life came except defeated life.
The Dauber felt shut in within a hedge,
Behind which form was hidden and thought was rife,
And that a blinding flash, a thrust, a knife
Would sweep the hedge away and make all plain,
Brilliant beyond all words, blinding the brain.

So the night past, but then no morning broke—
Only a something showed that night was dead.
A sea-bird, cackling like a devil, spoke,
And the fog drew away and hung like lead.
Like mighty cliffs it shaped, sullen and red;
Like glowering gods at watch it did appear,
And sometimes drew away, and then drew near.

Like islands, and like chasms, and like hell,
But always mighty and red, gloomy and ruddy,
Shutting the visible sea in like a well;

Slow heaving in vast ripples, blank and muddy,
Where the sun should have risen it streaked bloody.
The day was still-born; all the sea-fowl scattering
Splashed the still water, mewing, hovering, clattering.

Then Polar snow came down little and light,
Till all the sky was hidden by the small,
Most multitudinous drift of dirty white
Tumbling and wavering down and covering all—
Covering the sky, the sea, the clipper tall,
Furring the ropes with white, casing the mast,
Coming on no known air, but blowing past.

And all the air seemed full of gradual moan,
As though in those cloud-chasms the horns were blowing
The mort for gods cast out and overthrown,
Or for the eyeless sun plucked out and going.
Slow the low gradual moan came in the snowing;
The Dauber felt the prelude had begun.
The snowstorm fluttered by; he saw the sun

Show and pass by, gleam from one towering prison
Into another, vaster and more grim,
Which in dull crags of darkness had arisen
To muffle-to a final door on him.
The gods upon the dull crags lowered dim,
The pigeons chattered, quarrelling in the track.
In the south-west the dimness dulled to black.

Then came the cry of " Call all hands on deck! "
The Dauber knew its meaning; it was come:
Cape Horn, that tramples beauty into wreck,

And crumples steel and smites the strong man dumb.
Down clattered flying[1] kites and staysails: some
Sang out in quick, high calls; the fairleads[2] skirled,
And from the south-west came the end of the world.

"Caught in her ball-dress," said the Bosun, hauling:
"Lee-ay, lee-ay!" quick, high, came the men's call;
It was all wallop of sails and startled calling.
"Let fly!" "Let go!" "Clew up!"[3] and "Let go all!"
"Now up and make them fast!" "Here, give us a
        haul!"
"Now up and stow them! Quick! By God! we're
        done!"
The blackness crunched all memory of the sun.

"Up!" said the Mate. "Mizen topgallants. Hurry!"
The Dauber ran, the others ran, the sails
Slatted and shook; out of the black a flurry
Whirled in fine lines, tattering the edge to trails.
Painting and art and England were old tales
Told in some other life to that pale man,
Who struggled with white fear and gulped and ran.

He struck a ringbolt in his haste and fell—
Rose, sick with pain, half-lamed in his left knee;
He reached the shrouds[4] where clambering men pell-mell
Hustled each other up and cursed him; he
Hurried aloft with them: then from the sea

[1] Light upper sails.
[2] Rings by means of which the running rigging is led.
[3] To draw the lower ends of the sails to the upper yard to furl
them.
[4] Strong wire ropes to resist the side strain on the mast.

Came a cold, sudden breath that made the hair
Stiff on the neck, as though Death whispered there.

JOHN MASEFIELD

THE VOYAGE

I

We left behind the painted buoy
    That tosses at the harbour mouth;
And madly danced our hearts with joy,
    As fast we fleeted to the South:
How fresh was every sight and sound
    On open main or winding shore!
We knew the merry world was round,
    And we might sail for evermore.

II

Warm broke the breeze against the brow,
    Dry sang the tackle, sang the sail:
The Lady's-head upon the prow
    Caught the shrill salt, and sheer'd the gale.
The broad seas swell'd to meet the keel,
    And swept behind: so quick the run,
We felt the good ship shake and reel,
    We seem'd to sail into the sun!

III

How oft we saw the Sun retire,
    And burn the threshold of the night,

Fall from his Ocean-lane of fire,
   And sleep beneath his pillar'd light!
How oft the purple-skirted robe
   Of twilight slowly downward drawn,
As thro' the slumber of the globe
   Again we dash'd into the dawn!

IV

New stars all night above the brim
   Of waters lighten'd into view;
They climb'd as quickly, for the rim
   Changed every moment as we flew.
Far ran the naked moon across
   The houseless ocean's heaving field,
Or flying shone, the silver boss
   Of her own halo's dusky shield;

V

The peaky islet shifted shapes,
   High towns on hills were dimly seen,
We past long lines of Northern capes
   And dewy Northern meadows green.
We came to warmer waves, and deep
   Across the boundless east we drove,
Where those long swells of breaker sweep
   The nutmeg rocks and isles of clove.

VI

By peaks that flamed, or, all in shade,
   Gloom'd the low coast and quivering brine

With ashy rains, that spreading made
  Fantastic plume or sable pine;
By sands and steaming flats, and floods
  Of mighty mouth, we scudded fast,
And hills and scarlet-mingled woods
  Glow'd for a moment as we past.

VII

O hundred shores of happy climes,
  How swiftly stream'd ye by the bark!
At times the whole sea burn'd, at times
  With wakes of fire we tore the dark;
At times a carven craft would shoot
  From havens hid in fairy bowers,
With naked limbs and flowers and fruit,
  But we nor paused for fruit nor flowers.

VIII

For one fair Vision ever fled
  Down the waste waters day and night,
And still we follow'd where she led,
  In hope to gain upon her flight.
Her face was evermore unseen,
  And fixt upon the far sea-line;
But each man murmur'd " O my Queen,
  I follow till I make thee mine."

IX

And now we lost her, now she gleam'd
  Like Fancy made of golden air,

Now nearer to the prow she seem'd
  Like Virtue firm, like Knowledge fair,
Now high on waves that idly burst
  Like Heavenly Hope she crown'd the sea,
And now, the bloodless point reversed,
  She bore the blade of Liberty.

X

And only one among us—him
  We pleased not—he was seldom pleased:
He saw not far: his eyes were dim:
  But ours he swore were all diseased.
"A ship of fools" he shriek'd in spite,
  "A ship of fools" he sneer'd and wept.
And overboard one stormy night
  He cast his body, and on we swept.

XI

And never sail of ours was furl'd,
  Nor anchor dropt at eve or morn;
We loved the glories of the world,
  But laws of nature were our scorn;
For blasts would rise and rave and cease,
  But whence were those that drove the sail
Across the whirlwind's heart of peace,
  And to and thro' the counter-gale?

XII

Again to colder climes we came,
  For still we follow'd where she led:

Now mate is blind and captain lame,
  And half the crew are sick or dead.
But blind or lame or sick or sound
  We follow that which flies before:
We know the merry world is round,
  And we may sail for evermore.

LORD TENNYSON

MERRIMENT

SIR SMASHAM UPPE

Good afternoon, Sir Smasham Uppe!
We're having tea: do take a cup!
Sugar and milk? Now let me see—
Two lumps, I think? . . . Good gracious me!
The silly thing slipped off your knee!
Pray don't apologize, old chap:
A very trivial mishap!
So clumsy of you? How absurd!
My dear Sir Smasham, not a word!
Now do sit down and have another,
And tell us all about your brother—
You know, the one who broke his head.
Is the poor fellow still in bed?—
A chair—allow me, sir! . . . Great Scott!
That *was* a nasty smash! Eh, what?
Oh, not at all: the chair was old—
Queen Anne, or so we have been told.
We've got at least a dozen more:
Just leave the pieces on the floor.
I want you to admire our view:
Come nearer to the window, do;
And look how beautiful . . . Tut, tut!

You didn't see that it was shut?
I hope you are not badly cut!
Not hurt?   A fortunate escape!
Amazing!   Not a single scrape!
And now, if you have finished tea,
I fancy you might like to see
A little thing or two I've got.
That china plate?   Yes, worth a lot:
A beauty too . . . Ah, there it goes!
I trust it didn't hurt your toes?
Your elbow brushed it off the shelf?
Of course: I've done the same myself.
And now, my dear Sir Smasham—Oh,
You surely don't intend to go?
You *must* be off?   Well, come again.
So glad you're fond of porcelain!

E. V. RIEU

TARANTELLA

Do you remember an Inn,
Miranda?
Do you remember an Inn?
And the tedding and the spreading
Of the straw for a bedding,
And the fleas that tease in the High Pyrenees,
And the wine that tasted of the tar?
And the cheers and the jeers of the young
    muleteers
(Under the vine of the dark verandah)?
Do you remember an Inn, Miranda,
Do you remember an Inn?

And the cheers and the jeers of the young
    muleteers
Who hadn't got a penny,
And who weren't paying any,
And the hammer at the doors and the Din?
And the Hip! Hop! Hap!
Of the clap
Of the hands to the twirl and the swirl
Of the girl gone chancing,
Glancing,
Dancing,
Backing and advancing,
Snapping of the clapper to the spin
Out and in——
And the Ting, Tong, Tang of the Guitar!
Do you remember an Inn,
Miranda?
Do you remember an Inn?

Never more;
Miranda,
Never more.
Only the high peaks hoar:
And Aragon a torrent at the door.
No sound
In the walls of the Halls where falls
The tread
Of the feet of the dead to the ground.
No sound:
But the boom
Of the far Waterfall like Doom.

HILAIRE BELLOC

JOLLY GOOD ALE AND OLD
(*From " Gammer Gurton's Needle "*[1])

I cannot eat but little meat,
   My stomach is not good;
But sure I think that I can drink
   With him that wears a hood.
Though I go bare, take ye no care,
   I nothing am a-cold;
I stuff my skin so full within
   Of jolly good ale and old.
      Back and side go bare, go bare;
      Both foot and hand go cold;
      But, belly, God send thee good ale enough,
      Whether it be new or old.

I love no roast but a nut-brown toast,
   And a crab laid in the fire;
A little bread shall do me stead;
   Much bread I not desire.
No frost nor snow, no wind, I trow,
   Can hurt me if I would;
I am so wrapp'd and thoroughly lapp'd
   Of jolly good ale and old.
      Back and side go bare, go bare, etc.

And Tib, my wife, that as her life
   Loveth well good ale to seek,

---

[1] This is the second English comedy in verse. The first was
" Ralph Roister Doister."

Full oft drinks she till ye may see
    The tears run down her cheek:
Then doth she trowl to me the bowl
    Even as a maltworm should,
And saith, " Sweetheart, I took my part
    Of this jolly good ale and old."
        Back and side go bare, go bare, etc.

Now let them drink till they nod and wink,
    Even as good fellows should do;
They shall not miss to have the bliss
    Good ale doth bring men to;
And all poor souls that have scour'd bowls
    Or have them lustily troll'd,
God save the lives of them and their wives,
    Whether they be young or old.
        Back and side go bare, go bare;
        Both foot and hand go cold;
        But, belly, God send thee good ale enough,
        Whether it be new or old.

                    JOHN STILL

THE PRIEST AND THE MULBERRY-TREE

Did you hear of the curate who mounted his mare.
And merrily trotted along to the fair?
Of creature more tractable none ever heard:
In the height of her speed she would stop at a word;
But again with a word, when the curate said, " Hey,"
She put forth her mettle and galloped away.

As near to the gates of the city he rode,
While the sun of September all brilliantly glowed,
The good priest discover'd, with eyes of desire,
A mulberry-tree in a hedge of wild-briar;
On boughs long and lofty, in many a green shoot,
Hung, large, black, and glossy, the beautiful fruit.

The curate was hungry, and thirsty to boot;
He shrank from the thorns, though he longed for the
     fruit;
With a word he arrested his courser's keen speed,
And he stood up erect on the back of his steed;
On the saddle he stood while the creature stood still,
And he gathered the fruit till he took his good fill.

" Sure never," he thought, " was a creature so rare,
So docile, so true, as my excellent mare;
Lo, here, how I stand," (and he gazed all around),
" As safe and as steady as if on the ground;
Yet how had it been, if some traveller this way,
Had, dreaming no mischief, but chanced to cry ' Hey '? "

He stood with his head in the mulberry-tree,
And he spoke out aloud in his fond reverie;
At the sound of the word the good mare made a push,
And down went the priest in the wild-briar bush.
He remembered too late, on his thorny green bed,
Much that well may be thought, cannot wisely be said.

THOMAS LOVE PEACOCK

HILDEBRAND

*Who was frightened by a Passing Motor,
and was brought to Reason*

"Oh, murder! What was that, Papa!"
"My child, it was a motor-car,
A most ingenious toy!
Designed to captivate and charm
Much, rather than to rouse alarm
In any English boy.

"What would your Great Grandfather, who
Was aide-de-camp to General Brue,
And lost a leg at Waterloo,
And Quatre-Bras and Ligny too!
And died at Trafalgar!
What would he have remarked to hear
His young descendant shriek with fear,
Because he happened to be near
A harmless motor-car!
But do not fret about it! Come!
We'll off to Town and purchase some!"

HILAIRE BELLOC

ODE TO TOBACCO

Thou who, when fears attack,
Bidst them avaunt, and Black
Care, at the horseman's back
    Perching, unseatest;

Sweet, when the morn is grey;
Sweet, when they've cleared away
Lunch; and at close of day
    Possibly sweetest:

I have a liking old
For thee, though manifold
Stories, I know, are told,
    Not to thy credit;
How one (or two at most)
Drops make a cat a ghost—
Useless, except to roast—
    Doctors have said it:

How they who use fusees
All grow by slow degrees
Brainless as chimpanzees,
    Meagre as lizards:
Go mad, and beat their wives;
Plunge (after shocking lives)
Razors and carving knives
    Into their gizzards.

Confound such knavish tricks!
Yet know I five or six
Smokers who freely mix
    Still with their neighbours;
Jones—(who, I'm glad to say,
Asked leave of Mrs. J.)—
Daily absorbs a clay
    After his labours.

Cats may have had their goose
Cooked by tobacco-juice;
Still why deny its use
  Thoughtfully taken?
We're not as tabbies are:
Smith, take a fresh cigar!
Jones, the tobacco-jar!
  Here's to thee, Bacon!

CHARLES STUART CALVERLEY

A MUSICAL AT-HOME

A little party in the house—
The first to come is Mr. Grouse.
And he has hardly settled down
When they announce Sir Fractious Frown;
And, just as talk is getting slack,
My Lord and Lady Answer Back.
This *is* a pleasure: I am proud.
Step in: you'll find we're quite a crowd.
And Mrs. Contradict, I see,
Is just behind you: pardon me!
Another ring. Ah, Lady Snap,
Permit me to remove your wrap.
How good of you to come so far
And bring the Grumbles in your car!—
Now bless my soul, I know that face!
And yet—of course, it's Miss Grimace.
These fashions alter people so!
Come in and take your hat off. No?
And who's this trotting up the stair?

Little Miss Quarrel, I declare!
So musical, so quick, so merry,
And clever with her fingers—very!
Ah, Mr. Bump, good afternoon!
I thought we might expect you soon.
Another knock. Dear Major Punch,
Most kind of you to rush your lunch!
Let me present Miss Whack. You've met her?
Old friends, you say? So much the better!
Lord Biff—allow me—Canon Batt.
At school together? Fancy that!
The world is really very small.
Excuse me—someone in the hall.
Aha, the gallant Captain Kick!
Late? Not at all. You're in the nick.
And you, Miss Shindy, come along:
We're counting on you for a song.
And now I think we're nearly done—
All here and happy—but for one.
Ah, Mrs. Tears, how *do* you do?
So glad you've brought your music too!
What dreadful weather! Do come in.
And now we might as well begin.

E. V. RIEU

JOURNEYS AND ENCOUNTERS

LONDON TO PARIS, BY AIR

I

The droning roar is quickened, and we lift
On steady wing, like upward sweep of air,
Into the fleece-strewn heaven.   The great plane
Draws to herself the leagues : onward we bear
In one resistless eddy towards the south
Over the English fields, trim-hedged and square,
And countless, winding lanes, a vast expanse
Of flattened green : huge shapes of shadow float
Inconsequent as bubbles : haunts of men
Stripped of their cherished privacy we note
And crawling multitudes within a town—
On all we rangers of the wind look down.

II

The coast-line swings to us : beneath our feet
The grey-green carpet of the sliding sea
Stretches afar, on it small, busy ships
Whose comet-tails in foamy whiteness flee :
We lift, and snowy cloudlets roam below,
Frail, wistful spirits of pure charity

Blessing the waters: like green marble veined,
The waves roll in upon the yellowing sand,
Then break to myriad, filmy curves of lace
Where they eternally caress the land:
Now low lies France—the kingdom of the breeze
Parts not the nations like the severing seas.

III

Down the wide river, jauntily outspread,
A fishing fleet comes seaward, to our eyes
Mere walnut shells with autumn leaves for sails:
And now a fellow pilgrim of the skies,
Like a big insect droning past our flank,
Cruises to England home: before us lies
The rolling plain with its great, hedgeless strips
Of close-tilled fields, red roofs, and pointed trees,
The feathered arrows of the long French roads,
And all the stretch of quiet harmonies:
Then haven shows, and downward to earth's breast,
Like homing bird, we wheel and sink to rest.

LORD GORELL

JOURNEY OF THE MAGI

" A cold coming we had of it,
Just the worst time of the year
For a journey, and such a long journey:
The ways deep, and the weather sharp,
The very dead of winter."
And the camels galled, sore-footed, refractory,

Lying down in the melting snow.
There were times we regretted
The summer palaces on slopes, the terraces,
And the silken girls bringing sherbet.
Then the camel men cursing and grumbling
And running away, and wanting their liquor and
  women,
And the night-fires going out, and the lack of shelters,
And the cities hostile and the towns unfriendly
And the villages dirty and charging high prices:
A hard time we had of it.
At the end we preferred to travel all night,
Sleeping in snatches,
With the voices singing in our ears, saying
That this was all folly.

Then at dawn we came down to a temperate valley,
Wet, below the snow-line, smelling of vegetation;
With a running stream and a water-mill beating the
  darkness,
And three trees on the low sky,
And an old white horse galloped away in the meadow.
Then we came to a tavern with vine-leaves over the
  lintel,
Six hands at an open door dicing for pieces of silver,
And feet kicking the empty wine-skins.
But there was no information, and so we continued
And arrived at evening, not a moment too soon
Finding the place; it was (you may say) satisfactory.

All this was a long time ago, I remember,
And I would do it again, but set down

This set down
This: were we led all that way for
Birth or Death? There was a Birth, certainly,
We had evidence and no doubt. I had seen birth and
    death,
But had thought they were different; this Birth was
Hard and bitter agony for us, like Death, our death.
We returned to our places, these Kingdoms,
But no longer at ease here, in the old dispensation,
With an alien people clutching their gods.
I should be glad of another death.

T. S. ELIOT

THE GOLDEN JOURNEY TO SAMARKAND[1]

PROLOGUE

We who with songs beguile your pilgrimage
    And swear that Beauty lives though lilies die,
We Poets of the proud old lineage
    Who sing to find your hearts, we know not why,—

What shall we tell you? Tales, marvellous tales
    Of ships and stars and isles where good men rest,
Where nevermore the rose of sunset pales,
    And winds and shadows fall toward the West:

And there the world's first huge white-bearded kings
    In dim glades sleeping, murmur in their sleep,

[1] A city of Russian Turkestan. The author spent two years in the consular service at Beirut.

And closer round their breasts the ivy clings,
  Cutting its pathway slow and red and deep.

II

And how beguile you? Death has no repose
  Warmer and deeper than that Orient sand
Which hides the beauty and bright faith of those
  Who made the Golden Journey to Samarkand.

And now they wait and whiten peaceably,
  Those conquerors, those poets, those so fair:
They know time comes, not only you and I,
  But the whole world shall whiten, here or there;

When those long caravans that cross the plain
  With dauntless feet and sound of silver bells
Put forth no more for glory or for gain,
  Take no more solace from the palm-girt wells.

When the great markets by the sea shut fast
  All that calm Sunday that goes on and on:
When even lovers find their peace at last,
  And Earth is but a star, that once had shone.

EPILOGUE
At the Gate of the Sun, Bagdad, in olden time

THE MERCHANTS (*together*)

Away, for we are ready to a man!
  Our camels sniff the evening and we are glad.

Lead on, O Master of the Caravan:
  Lead on the Merchant-Princes of Bagdad.

THE CHIEF DRAPER

Have we not Indian carpets dark as wine,
  Turbans and sashes, gowns and bows and veils,
And broideries of intricate design,
  And printed hangings in enormous bales?

THE CHIEF GROCER

We have rose-candy, we have spikenard,[1]
  Mastic[2] and terebinth[3] and oil and spice,
And such sweet jams meticulously jarred
  As God's own Prophet eats in Paradise.

THE PRINCIPAL JEWS

And we have manuscripts in peacock styles
  By Ali of Damascus; we have swords
Engraved with storks and apes and crocodiles,
  And heavy beaten necklaces, for Lords.

THE MASTER OF THE CARAVAN

But you are nothing but a lot of Jews.

THE PRINCIPAL JEWS

Sir, even dogs have daylight, and we pay.

THE MASTER OF THE CARAVAN

But who are ye in rags and rotten shoes,
  You dirty-bearded, blocking up the way?

[1] A fragrant oil.   [2] A resinous gum.   [3] Turpentine.

JAMES ELROY FLECKER

THE PILGRIMS

We are the Pilgrims, master; we shall go
   Always a little further: it may be
Beyond that last blue mountain barred with snow,
   Across that angry or that glimmering sea,
White on a throne or guarded in a cave
   There lives a prophet who can understand
Why men were born; but surely we are brave,
   Who make the Golden Journey to Samarkand.

THE CHIEF MERCHANT

We gnaw the nail of hurry. Master, away!

ONE OF THE WOMEN

  O turn your eyes to where your children stand.
Is not Bagdad the beautiful? O stay!

THE MERCHANTS (*in chorus*)

We take the Golden Road to Samarkand.

AN OLD MAN

Have you not girls and garlands in your homes,
   Eunuchs and Syrian boys at your command?
Seek not excess: God hateth him who roams!

THE MERCHANTS (*in chorus*)

We make the Golden Journey to Samarkand.

A PILGRIM WITH A BEAUTIFUL VOICE

Sweet to ride forth at evening from the wells
   When shadows pass gigantic on the sand,

And softly through the silence beat the bells
Along the Golden Road to Samarkand.

A MERCHANT

We travel not for trafficking alone:
By hotter winds our fiery hearts are fanned:
For lust of knowing what should not be known
We make the Golden Journey to Samarkand.

THE MASTER OF THE CARAVAN

Open the gate, O watchman of the night!

THE WATCHMAN

Ho, travellers, I open. For what land
Leave you the dim-moon city of delight?

THE MERCHANTS (*with a shout*)

We make the Golden Journey to Samarkand.

[The Caravan passes through the gate.]

THE WATCHMAN (*consoling the women*)

What would ye, ladies? It was ever thus.
Men are unwise and curiously planned.

A WOMAN

They have their dreams, and do not think of us.

VOICES OF THE CARAVAN (*in the distance, singing*)

We make the Golden Journey to Samarkand.

JAMES ELROY FLECKER

THE TASKS OF PSYCHE[1]

(From " Eros and Psyche ")

She took her then aside, and bade her heed
A heap of grains piled high upon the floor,
Millet and mustard, hemp and poppy seed,
And fern-bloom's undistinguishable spore,
All kinds of pulse, of grasses, and of spice,
Clover and linseed, rape, and corn, and rice,
Dodder, and sesame, and many more.

" Sort me these seeds," she said; " it now is night,
"I will return at morning; if I find
That thou hast separated all aright,
Each grain from other grain after its kind,
And set them in unmingl'd heaps apart,
Then shall thy wish be granted to thine heart."
Whereat she turn'd and closed the door behind.

A single lamp there stood beside the heap,
And shed thereon its mocking golden light;
Such as might tempt the weary eye to sleep
Rather than prick the nerve of taskèd sight.
Yet Psyche, not to fail for lack of zeal,
With good will sat her down to her ordeal,
Sorting the larger seeds as best she might.

[1] Bridges' poem " Eros and Psyche " is based on an episode in the
fable of the " Golden Ass " by Apuleius. Eros (Cupid) falls in love
with Psyche who incurs his wrath. She is subjected by Aphrodite
(Venus) to many hardships and tasks, two of which are narrated
in these stanzas.

When lo! upon the wall, a shadow passed
Of doubtful shape, across the chamber dim
Moving with speed: and seeing nought that cast
The shade, she bent her down the flame to trim;
And there the beast itself, a little ant,
Climb'd up in compass of the lustre scant,
Upon the bowl of oil ran round the rim.

Smiling to see the creature of her fear
So dwarf'd by truth, she watcht him where he crept,
For mere distraction telling in his ear
What straits she then was in, and telling wept.
Whereat he stood and trim'd his horns; but ere
Her tale was done resumed his manner scare,
Ran down, and on his way in darkness kept.

But she intent drew forth with dextrous hand
The larger seeds, or pushed the smaller back,
Or light from heavy with her breathing fanned.
When suddenly she saw the floor grow black,
And troops of ants flowing in noiseless train,
Moved to the hill of seeds, as o'er a plain
Armies approach a city for attack;

And gathering on the grain, began to strive
With grappling horns; and each from out the heap
His burden drew, and all their motion live
Struggled and slid upon the surface steep.
And Psyche wonder'd, watching them, to find
The creatures separated kind from kind:
Till dizzied with the sight she fell asleep.

124

And when she woke 'twas with the morning sound
Of Aphrodite's anger at the door,
Whom high amaze stayed backward, as she found
Her foe asleep with all her trouble o'er;
And round the room beheld, in order due,
The piles arranged distinct and sorted true,
Grain with grain, seed with seed, and spore with
     spore.

She fiercely cried, " Thou shalt not thus escape;
For to this marvel dar'st thou not pretend.
There is but one that could this order shape,
Demeter,[1]—but I knew her not thy friend.
Therefore another trial will I set,
In which she cannot aid thee or abet,
But thou thyself must bring it fair to end."

Thereon she sped her to the bounds of Thrace,
And set her by a river deep and wide,
And said " To east beyond this stream, a race
Of golden-fleecèd sheep at pasture bide.
Go seek them out; and this thy task, to pull
But one lock for me of their precious wool
And give it in my hands at eventide:

This do and thou shalt have thy heart's desire."
Which said, she fled and left her by the stream:
And Psyche then, with courage still entire
Had plunged therein; but now of great esteem
Her life she rated, while it lent a spell
Wherein she yet might hope to quit her well,
And in one winning all her woes redeem.

[1] The Earth Goddess.

There as she stood in doubt, a fluting voice
Rose from the flood, " Psyche, be not afraid
To hear a reed give tongue, for 'twas of choice
That I from mortal flesh a plant was made.
My name is Syrinx:[1] once from mighty Pan
Into the drowning river as I ran,
The change I begged my steps for ever stayed.

But for that change in many climes I live;
And Pan, my lover, who to me alone
Is true and does me honour, I forgive—
Nor, if I speak in sorrow, is't my own;
Rather for thee my voice I now uplift
To warn thee, plunge not in the river swift,
Nor seek the golden sheep to men unknown.

If thou should cross the stream, which may not be,
Thou couldst not climb upon the hanging rocks,
Nor ever, as the goddess bade thee, see
The pasture of the yellow-fleecèd flocks:
Or if thou could, their herded horns would gore
And slay thee on the crags, or thrust thee o'er
Ere thou couldst rob them of their golden locks.

The goddess means thy death. But I can show
How thy obedience yet may thwart her will.
At noon the golden flocks descend below,
Leaving the scented herbage of the hill,
And where the shelving banks to shallows fall,
Drink at the rippling waters one and all,
Nor back return till they have drawn their fill.

[1] A Greek word meaning a reed or pipe.

126

I will command a thorn bush, that it stoop
Over some ram that steppeth by in peace,
And him in all its prickles firmly coop,
Making thee seizure of his golden fleece;
So without peril of his angry horns
Shalt thou be quit: for he upon the thorns
Must leave his ransom ere he win release."

Then Psyche thanked her for her kind befriending,
And hid among the rushes looking east;
And when noon came she saw the flock descending
Out of the hills; and, lo! one golden beast
Caught in a thorn bush; and the mighty brute
Struggled and tore from its twisted root
Into the stream, or e'er he was released.

And when they watered were and gone, the breeze
Floated the freighted thorn where Psyche lay:
Whence she unhooked the golden wool at ease,
And back to heaven for passage swift gan pray.
And Hermes,[1] who was sent to be her guide
If so she lived, came down at eventide,
And bore her thither ere the close of day.

ROBERT BRIDGES

[1] The messenger of the gods.

THE DAEMON LOVER

" O where have you been, my long, long love,
    This long seven years and more? "—
" O I'm come to seek my former vows
    Ye granted me before."—

" O hold your tongue of your former vows,
   For they will breed sad strife;
O hold your tongue of your former vows,
   For I am become a wife."

He turned him right and round about,
   And the tear blinded his ee;
" I wad never hae trodden on Irish ground,
   If it had not been for thee.

I might hae had a king's daughter,
   Far, far beyond the sea;
I might have had a king's daughter,
   Had it not been for love o' thee."

" If ye might have had a king's daughter,
   Yer sell ye had to blame;
Ye might have taken the king's daughter,
   For ye kend that I was nane!

If I was to leave my husband dear,
   And my two babes also,
O what have you to take me to,
   If with you I should go? "

" I hae seven ships upon the sea;
   The eighth brought me to land,
With four and twenty bold mariners,
   And music on every hand."

She has taken up her two little babes,
   Kissed them both cheek and chin;

" O fare ye well, my own two babes,
   For I'll never see you again."

She set her foot upon the ship;
   No mariners could she behold,
But the sails were o' the taffetie,
   And the masts o' the beaten gold.

She had not sailed a league, a league,
   A league but barely three,
When dismal grew his countenance,
   And drumlie[1] grew his ee.

They had not sailed a league, a league,
   A league but barely three,
Until she espied his cloven foot,
   And she wept right bitterly.

" O hold your tongue of your weeping," says he,
   " Of your weeping now let me be;
I will show you how the lilies grow
   On the banks of Italy! "—

" O what hills are yon, yon pleasant hills,
   That the sun shines sweetly on? "
" O yon are the hills of heaven," he said,
   " Where you will never win."—

" O whaten a mountain is yon," she said,
   " All so dreary wi' frost and snow? "

[1] Gloomy.

" O yon is the mountain of hell," he cried,
  " Where you and I will go."

He strack the tap-mast wi' his hand,
  The fore-mast wi' his knee;
And he brake that gallant ship in twain,
  And sank her in the sea.

ANONYMOUS

THE DOUGLAS TRAGEDY

"Rise up, rise up, now Lord Douglas," she says,
  "And put on your armour so bright;
Let it never be said that a daughter of thine
  Was married to a lord under night.

"Rise up, rise up, my seven bold sons,
  And put on your armour so bright,
And take better care of your youngest sister,
  For your eldest's awa the last night."—

He's mounted her on a milk-white steed,
  And himself on a dapple grey,
With a bugelet horn hung down his side;
  And lightly they rode away.

Lord William look'd o'er his left shoulder,
  To see what he could see,
And there he spy'd her seven brethren bold
  Come riding over the lea.

"Light down, light down, Lady Margret," he said,
  "And hold my steed in your hand,
Until that against your seven brethren bold,
  And your father, I mak' a stand."—

O, there she stood, and bitter she stood,
  And never did shed one tear,
Until that she saw her seven brethren fa',
  And her father, who lov'd her so dear.

"O hold your hand, Lord William!" she said,
  "For your strokes thcy are wondrous sair;
True lovers I can get many an ane,
  But a father I can never get mair."—

O she's ta'en out her handkerchief,
  It was o' the holland sae fine,
And aye she dighted her father's wounds,
  That were redder than the wine.

"O chuse, O chuse, Lady Margret," he said,
  "O whether will ye gang or bide?"
"I'll gang, I'll gang, Lord William," she said,
  "For ye've left me no other guide."—

He's lifted her on a milk-white steed,
  And himself on a dapple grey,
With a bugelet horn hung down by his side;
  And slowly they baith rade away.

O they rade on, and on they rade,
  And a' by the light of the moon,

Until they came to yon wan water,
   And there they lighted doun.

They lighted doun to tak' a drink
   Of the spring that ran sae clear,
And doun the stream ran his gude heart's blood,
   And sair she 'gan to fear.

"Hold up, hold up, Lord William," she says,
   "For I fear that you are slain."—
"'Tis naething but the shadow of my scarlet cloak,
   That shines in the water sae plain."—

O they rade on, and on they rade,
   And a' by the light of the moon,
Until they cam' to his mother's ha' door,
   And there they lighted doun.

"Get up, get up, lady mother," he says,
   "Get up, and let me in!—
Get up, get up, lady mother," he says,
   "For this night my fair lady I've win.

"O mak my bed, lady mother," he says,
   "O mak it braid and deep,
And lay Lady Margret close at my back,
   And the sounder I will sleep."

Lord William was dead lang ere midnight,
   Lady Margret lang ere day,—
And all true lovers that go thegither,
   May they have mair luck than they!

Lord William was buried in St. Mary's kirk,
  Lady Margret in Mary's quire;
Out o' the lady's grave grew a bonny red rose,
  And out o' the knight's a brier.

And they twa met, and they twa plat,[1]
  And fain they wad be near;
And a' the warld might ken right weel.
  They were twa lovers dear.

But bye and rade the Black Douglas,
  And wow but he was rough!
For he pull'd up the bonny brier,
  And flang't in St. Mary's Lough.

[1] Pleated together.

EDOM O' GORDON[1]

It fell about the Martinmas,
  When the wind blew shrill and cauld,
Said Edom o' Gordon to his men,
  "We maun draw to a hauld.

"And what a hauld sall we draw to,
  My merry men and me?
We will gae to the house o' the Rodes,
  To see that fair ladye."

[1] Adam or Edom o' Gordon was a Berwickshire freebooter.

133

The lady stood on her castle wa',
   Beheld baith dale and down;
There she was 'ware of a host of men
   Cam' riding towards the town.

"O see ye not, my merry men a',
   O see ye not what I see?
Methinks I see a host of men;
   I marvel wha they be."

She ween'd it had been her lovely lord,
   As he cam riding hame;
It was the traitor, Edom o' Gordon,
   Wha reck'd nae sin nor shame.

She had nae sooner buskit[1] hersell,
   And putten on her gown,
But Edom o' Gordon an' his men
   Were round about the town.

They had nae sooner supper set,
   Nae sooner said the grace,
But Edom o' Gordon an' his men
   Were lighted about the place.

The lady ran up to her tower-head,
   Sae fast as she could hie,
To see if by her fair speeches
   She could wi' him agree.

"Come doun to me, ye lady gay,
   Come doun, come doun to me;

[1] Dressed.

134

This night sall ye lig within mine arms,
   To-morrow my bride sall be."—

"I winna come down, ye fals Gordon,
   I winna come down to thee;
I winna forsake my ain dear lord,
   That is sae far frae me."—

"Gie owre your house, ye lady fair,
   Gie owre your house to me;
Or I sall brenn yoursel therein,
   But and your babies three."—

"I winna gie owre, ye fals Gordon,
   To nae sic traitor as yee;
And if ye brenn my ain dear babes,
   My lord sall mak ye dree.

"Now reach my pistol, Glaud, my man,
   And charge ye weel my gun;
For, but an I pierce that bluidy butcher,
   My babes, we been undone!"

She stood upon her castle wa',
   And let twa bullets flee:
She miss'd that bluidy butcher's heart,
   And only razed his knee.

"Set fire to the house!" quo' fals Gordon,
   All wud wi' dule and ire:
"Fals lady, ye sall rue this deid
   As ye brenn in the fire!"—

" Wae worth, wae worth ye, Jock, my man!
  I paid ye weel your fee;
Why pu' ye out the grund-wa' stane,
  Lets in the reek to me?

" And e'en wae worth ye, Jock, my man!
  I paid ye weel your hire;
Why pu' ye out the grund-wa' stane,
  To me lets in the fire? "—

" Ye paid me weel my hire, ladye,
  Ye paid me weel my fee:
But now I'm Edom o' Gordon's man,
  Maun either do or dee."

O then bespake her little son,
  Sat on the nurse's knee:
Says, " Mither dear, gie owre this house,
  For the reek it smithers me."—

" I wad gie a' my gowd, my bairn,
  Sae wad I a' my fee,
Fa ae blast o' the western wind,
  To blaw the reek frae thee."

O then bespake her dochter dear—
  She was baith jimp[1] and sma':
" O row me in a pair o' sheets,
  And tow me owre the wa'! "

They row'd her in a pair o' sheets,
  And tow'd her owre the wa';

[1] Slender.

136

But on the point o' Gordon's spear
   She gat a deadly fa'.

O bonnie, bonnie was her mouth,
   And cherry were her cheiks,
And clear, clear was her yellow hair,
   Whereon the red blood dreips.

Then wi' his spear he turn'd her owre;
   O gin her face was wane!
He said, "Ye are the first that e'er
   I wish'd alive again."

He turn'd her owre and owre again;
   O gin her skin was white!
"I might hae spared that bonnie face
   To hae been some man's delight.

"Busk[1] and boun, my merry men a',
   For ill dooms I do guess;
I canna look in that bonnie face
   As it lies on the grass."—

"Wha looks to freits, my master dear,
   It's freits will follow them;
Let it ne'er be said that Edom o' Gordon
   Was daunted by a dame."

But when the lady saw the fire
   Come flaming owre her head,
She wept, and kiss'd her children twain,
   Says, "Bairns, we been but dead."

[1] Dress and prepare.

The Gordon then his bugle blew,
    And said, "Awa', Awa'!
This house o' the Rodes is a' in a flame;
    I hauld it time to ga'."

And this way lookit her ain dear lord,
    As he cam owre the lea;
He saw his castle a' in a lowe,
    As far as he could see.

Then sair, O sair, his mind misgave,
    And all his heart was wae:
"Put on, put on, my wighty men,
    Sae fast as ye can gae.

"Put on, put on, my wighty men,
    Sae fast as ye can drie!
For he that's hindmost o' the thrang
    Sall ne'er get good o' me."

Then some they rade, and some they ran,
    Out-owre the grass and bent;
But ere the foremost could win up,
    Baith lady and babes were brent.

And after the Gordon he is gane,
    Sae fast as he might drie;
And soon i' the Gordon's foul heart's blude
    He's wroken his dear ladye.

ANONYMOUS

EDWARD

" Why does your brand so drop wi' blood,
          Edward, Edward,
Why does your brand so drop wi' blood,
  And why so sad go ye O? "
" O I have killed my hawk so good,
          Mother, mother,
O I have killed my hawk so good,
  And I had no more but he O."

" Your hawk's blood was never so red,
          Edward, Edward,
Your hawk's blood was never so red,
  My dear son I tell thee O."
" O I have killed my red-roan steed,
          Mother, mother,
O I have killed my red-roan steed,
  That erst was so fair and free O."

" Your steed was old, and ye have got more,
          Edward, Edward,
Your steed was old, and ye have got more.
  Some other dool you drie O."
" O I have killed my father dear,
          Mother, mother,
O I have killed my father dear,
  Alas, and woe is me O! "

" And what penance will ye drie for that,
          Edward, Edward?
And what penance will ye drie for that?
  My dear son, now tell me O."

"I'll set my foot in yonder boat,
  Mother, mother,
I'll set my foot in yonder boat,
  And I'll fare over the sea O."

"And what will ye do wi' your towers and your hall,
  Edward, Edward?
And what will ye do wi' your towers and your hall?
  That were so fair to see O?"
"I'll let them stand till they down fall,
  Mother, mother,
I'll let them stand till they down fall,
  For here nevermore may I be O."

"And what will ye leave to your bairns and your wife,
  Edward, Edward?
And what will ye leave to your bairns and your wife,
  When ye go over the sea O?"
"The world's wide, let them beg through life,
  Mother, mother,
The world's wide, let them beg through life,
  For them never more will I see O."

"And what will ye leave to your own mother dear?
  Edward, Edward?
And what will ye leave to your own mother dear?
  My dear son, now tell me O."
"The curse of hell from me shall ye bear,
  Mother, mother,
The curse of hell from me shall ye bear,
  Such counsels ye gave to me O."

ANONYMOUS

140

THE BULL FIGHT

(*From " Childe Harold's Pilgrimage "*[1])

In costly sheen and gaudy cloak array'd,
But all afoot, the light-limb'd Matadore
Stands in the centre, eager to invade
The lord of lowing herds; but not before
The ground, with cautious tread, is traversed o'er,
Lest aught unseen should lurk to thwart his speed:
His arms a dart, he fights aloof, nor more
Can man achieve without the friendly steed—
Alas! too oft condemn'd for him to bear and bleed.

Thrice sounds the clarion; lo! the signal falls,
The den expands, and Expectation mute
Gapes round the silent circle's peopled walls,
Bounds with one lashing spring the mighty brute,
And, wildly staring, spurns, with sounding foot,
The sand, nor blindly rushes on his foe:
Here, there, he points his threatening front, to suit
His first attack, wide waving to and fro
His angry tail; red rolls his eye's dilated glow.

Sudden he stops; his eye is fix'd: away,
Away, thou heedless boy! prepare the spear:
Now is thy time to perish, or display
The skill that yet may check his mad career.
With well-timed croupe the nimble coursers veer;

---

[1] The poem describes the travels of a pilgrim who seeks distraction in foreign lands. Byron recalls the historical associations of the places his hero visits.

On foams the bull, but not unscathed he goes;
Streams from his flank the crimson torrent clear:
He flies, he wheels, distracted with his throes;
Dart follows dart; lance, lance; loud bellowings speak his
    woes.

Again he comes; nor dart nor lance avail,
Nor the wild plunging of the tortured horse;
Though man and man's avenging arms assail,
Vain are his weapons, vainer is his force.
One gallant steed is stretch'd a mangled corse;
Another, hideous sight! unseam'd appears,
His gory chest unveils life's panting source;
Though death-struck, still his feeble frame he rears;
Staggering, but stemming all, his lord unharm'd he
    bears.

Foil'd, bleeding, breathless, furious to the last,
Full in the centre stands the bull at bay,
Mid wounds, and clinging darts, and lances brast,
And foes disabled in the brutal fray;
And now the Matadores around him play,
Shake the red cloak and poise the ready brand:
Once more through all he bursts his thundering way—
Vain rage! the mantle quits the conynge hand,
Wraps his fierce eye—'tis past—he sinks upon the sand!

Where his vast neck just mingles with the spine,
Sheathed in his form the deadly weapon lies.
He stops—he starts—disdaining to decline:
Slowly he falls, amidst triumphant cries,
Without a groan, without a struggle dies.

The decorated car appears—on high
The corse is piled—sweet sight for vulgar eyes—
Four steeds that spurn the rein, as swift as shy,
Hurl the dark bulk along, scarce seen in dashing by.

LORD BYRON

BEFORE AGINCOURT

(From " Henry V ")

Westmoreland.
O! that we now had here
But one ten thousand of those men in England
That do no work to-day.
King Henry.   What's he that wishes so?
My cousin Westmoreland?   No, my fair cousin:
If we are mark'd to die, we are enow
To do our country loss; and if to live,
The fewer men, the greater share of honour.
God's will! I pray thee, wish not one man more.
By Jove, I am not covetous for gold,
Nor care I who doth feed upon my cost;
It yearns me not if men my garments wear;
Such outward things dwell not in my desires:
But if it be a sin to covet honour,
I am the most offending soul alive.
No, faith, my coz, wish not a man from England:
God's peace! I would not lose so great an honour
As one man more, methinks, would share from me,
For the best hope I have. O, do not wish one more!
Rather proclaim it, Westmoreland, through my host,

That he which hath no stomach to this fight,
Let him depart; his passport shall be made,
And crowns for convoy put into his purse:
We would not die in that man's company
That fears his fellowship to die with us.
This day is call'd the feast of Crispian:
He that outlives this day, and comes safe home,
Will stand a tip-toe when this day is nam'd,
And rouse him at the name of Crispian.
He that shall live this day, and see old age,
Will yearly on the vigil feast his neighbours,
And say, "To-morrow is Saint Crispian":[1]
Then will he strip his sleeve and show his scars,
And say, "These wounds I had on Crispin's day."
Old men forget: yet all shall be forgot,
But he'll remember with advantages
What feats he did that day. Then shall our names,
Familiar in his mouth as household words,
Harry the king, Bedford and Exeter,
Warwick and Talbot, Salisbury and Gloucester,
Be in their flowing cups freshly remember'd.
This story shall the good man teach his son;
And Crispin Crispian shall ne'er go by,
From this day to the ending of the world,
But we in it shall be rememberèd;
We few, we happy few, we band of brothers;
For he to-day that sheds his blood with me
Shall be my brother; be he ne'er so vile
This day shall gentle his condition:

---

[1] October 25th, the day of the brother-saints, Crispin and Crispian, who left Rome for Soissons where they preached Christianity and earned a living by shoemaking.

And gentlemen in England, now a-bed,
Shall think themselves accurs'd they were not here,
And hold their manhoods cheap whiles any speaks
That fought with us upon Saint Crispin's day.

WILLIAM SHAKESPEARE

THE EVE OF WATERLOO

(*From " Childe Harold's Pilgrimage "*)

There was a sound of revelry by night,
And Belgium's capital had gather'd then
Her Beauty and her Chivalry, and bright
The lamps shone o'er fair women and brave men;
A thousand hearts beat happily; and when
Music arose with its voluptuous swell,
Soft eyes look'd love to eyes which spake again,
And all went merry as a marriage bell;
But hush! hark! a deep sound strikes like a rising knell!

Did ye not hear it?—No; 'twas but the wind,
Or the car rattling o'er the stony street;
On with the dance! let joy be unconfined;
No sleep till morn, when Youth and Pleasure meet
To chase the glowing Hours with flying feet—
But hark!—that heavy sound breaks in once more,
As if the clouds its echo would repeat;
And nearer, clearer, deadlier than before!
Arm! Arm! It is—it is—the cannon's opening roar!

Within a window'd niche of that high hall
Sate Brunswick's fated chieftain; he did hear

That sound the first amidst the festival,
And caught its tone with Death's prophetic ear;
And when they smiled because he deem'd it near,
His heart more truly knew that peal too well
Which stretch'd his father on a bloody bier,
And roused the vengeance blood alone could quell;
He rush'd into the field, and, foremost fighting, fell.

Ah! then and there was hurrying to and fro,
And gathering tears, and tremblings of distress,
And cheeks all pale, which but an hour ago
Blush'd at the praise of their own loveliness;
And there were sudden partings, such as press
The life from out young hearts, and choking sighs
Which ne'er might be repeated; who could guess
If ever more should meet those mutual eyes,
Since upon night so sweet such awful morn could rise!

And there was mounting in hot haste: the steed,
The mustering squadron, and the clattering car,
Went pouring forward with impetuous speed,
And swiftly forming in the ranks of war;
And the deep thunder peal on peal afar;
And near, the beat of the alarming drum
Roused up the soldier ere the morning star;
While throng'd the citizens with terror dumb,
Or whispering, with white lips—" The foe! they come!
    they come! "

And wild and high the " Cameron's gathering " rose!
The war-note of Lochiel, which Albyn's[1] hills

[1] The Celtic name for Scotland.

Have heard, and heard, too, have her Saxon foes:—
How in the noon of night that pibroch thrills,
Savage and shrill!   But with the breath which fills
Their mountain-pipe, so fill the mountaineers
With the fierce native daring which instils
The stirring memory of a thousand years,
And Evan's, Donald's fame rings in each clansman's
    ears!

And Ardennes waves above them her green leaves,
Dewy with nature's tear-drops as they pass,
Grieving, if aught inanimate e'er grieves,
Over the unreturning brave,—alas!
Ere evening to be trodden like the grass
Which now beneath them, but above shall grow
In its next verdure, when this fiery mass
Of living valour, rolling on the foe
And burning with high hope shall moulder cold and
    low.

Last noon beheld them full of lusty life,
Last eve in Beauty's circle proudly gay,
The midnight brought the signal-sound of strife,
The morn the marshalling in arms,—the day
Battle's magnificently stern array!
The thunder-clouds close o'er it, which when rent
The earth is cover'd thick with other clay,
Which her own clay shall cover, heap'd and pent,
Rider and horse,—friend, foe,—in one red burial blent!

LORD BYRON

SOHRAB MEETS RUSTUM[1]

(From " Sohrab and Rustum ")

But Rustum strode to his tent door, and call'd
His followers in, and bade them bring his arms,
And clad himself in steel: the arms he chose
Were plain, and on his shield was no device,
Only his helm was rich, inlaid with gold,
And from the fluted spine atop a plume
Of horsehair wav'd, a scarlet horsehair plume.
So arm'd, he issued forth; and Ruksh, his horse,
Follow'd him, like a faithful hound, at heel—
Ruksh, whose renown was nois'd through all the earth,
The horse, whom Rustum on a foray once
Did in Bokhara[2] by the river find
A colt beneath its dam, and drove him home,
And rear'd him; a bright bay, with lofty crest;
Dight with a saddle-cloth of broider'd green
Crusted with gold, and on the ground were work'd
All beasts of chase, all beasts which hunters know:
So follow'd, Rustum left his tents, and cross'd
The camp, and to the Persian host appear'd.
And all the Persians knew him, and with shouts
Hail'd; but the Tartars knew not who he was.
And dear as the wet diver to the eyes
Of his pale wife who waits and weeps on shore,
By sandy Bahrein,[3] in the Persian Gulf,

[1] The Tartar host is attacking the Persians and Sohrab challenges the bravest of the Persian lords to meet him in single combat. Rustum, his father, takes up the challenge and faces his unknown son.

[2] An ancient city in Asiatic Russia.

[3] An island.

Plunging all day in the blue waves, at night,
Having made up his tale of precious pearls,
Rejoins her in their hut upon the sands—
So dear to the pale Persians Rustum came.

  And Rustum to the Persian front advanc'd,
And Sohrab arm'd in Haman's tent, and came.
And as afield the reapers cut a swathe
Down through the middle of a rich man's corn,
And on each side are squares of standing corn,
And in the midst a stubble, short and bare;
So on each side were squares of men, with spears
Bristling, and in the midst, the open sand.
And Rustum came upon the sand, and cast
His eyes towards the Tartar tents, and saw
Sohrab come forth, and eyed him as he came.

  As some rich woman, on a winter's morn,
Eyes through her silken curtains the poor drudge
Who with numb blacken'd fingers makes her fire—
At cock-crow, on a starlit winter's morn,
When the frost flowers the whiten'd window panes—
And wonders how she lives, and what the thoughts
Of that poor drudge may be; so Rustum eyed
The unknown adventurous youth, who from afar
Came seeking Rustum, and defying forth
All the most valiant chiefs: long he perus'd
His spirited air, and wonder'd who he was.
For very young he seem'd, tenderly rear'd;
Like some young cypress, tall, and dark, and straight
Which in a queen's secluded garden throws
Its slight dark shadow on the moonlit turf,
By midnight, to a bubbling fountain's sound—
So slender Sohrab seem'd, so softly rear'd.

And a deep pity enter'd Rustum's soul
As he beheld him coming; and he stood,
And beckon'd to him with his hand, and said:—
    "O thou young man, the air of Heaven is soft,
And warm, and pleasant; but the grave is cold.
Heaven's air is better than the cold dead grave.
Behold me: I am vast, and clad in iron,
And tried; and I have stood on many a field
Of blood, and I have fought with many a foe:
Never was that field lost, or that foe sav'd.
O Sohrab, wherefore wilt thou rush on death?
Be govern'd! Quit the Tartar host, and come
To Iran, and be as my son to me,
And fight beneath my banner till I die.
There are no youths in Iran brave as thou."
    So he spake, mildly: Sohrab heard his voice,
The mighty voice of Rustum; and he saw
His giant figure planted on the sand,
Sole, like some single tower, which a chief
Hath builded on the waste in former years
Against the robbers; and he saw that head,
Streak'd with its first grey hairs: hope fill'd his soul;
And he ran forward and embraced his knees,
And clasp'd his hand within his own, and said:—
    "Oh, by thy father's head! by thine own soul!
Art thou not Rustum? speak! art thou not he?"
    But Rustum ey'd askance the kneeling youth,
And turn'd away, and spake to his own soul:—
    "Ah me, I muse what this young fox may mean!
False, wily, boastful, are these Tartar boys.
For if I now confess this thing he asks,
And hide it not, but say: *Rustum is here!*

He will not yield indeed, nor quit our foes,
But he will find some pretext not to fight,
And praise my fame, and proffer courteous gifts,
A belt or sword perhaps, and go his way.
And on a feast-tide, in Afrasiab's hall,
In Samarcand, he will arise and cry:
'I challenged once, when the two armies camp'd
Beside the Oxus, all the Persian lords
To cope with me in single fight; but they
Shrank, only Rustum dar'd; then he and I
Changed gifts, and went on equal terms away.'
So will he speak, perhaps, while men applaud;
Then were the chiefs of Iran shamed through me."

And then he turn'd, and sternly spake aloud:—
"Rise! wherefore dost thou vainly question thus
Of Rustum? I am here, whom thou hast call'd
By challenge forth; make good thy vaunt, or yield!
Is it with Rustum only thou wouldst fight?
Rash boy, men look on Rustum's face and flee!
For well I know, that did great Rustum stand
Before thy face this day, and were reveal'd,
There would be then no talk of fighting more.
But being what I am, I tell thee this;
Do thou record it in thine inmost soul:
Either thou shalt renounce thy vaunt, and yield,
Or else thy bones shall strew this sand, till winds
Bleach them, or Oxus with his summer floods,
Oxus in summer wash them all away."

He spoke: and Sohrab answer'd, on his feet:—
"Art thou so fierce? Thou wilt not fright me so.
I am no girl, to be made pale by words.
Yet this thou hast said well, did Rustum stand

Here on this field, there were no fighting then.
But Rustum is far hence, and we stand here.
Begin! thou art more vast, more dread than I,
And thou art prov'd, I know, and I am young—
But yet success sways with the breath of Heaven.
And though thou thinkest that thou knowest sure
Thy victory, yet thou canst not surely know.
For we are all, like swimmers in the sea,
Pois'd on the top of a huge wave of Fate,
Which hangs uncertain to which side to fall.
And whether it will heave us up to land,
Or whether it will roll us out to sea,
Back out to sea, to the deep waves of death,
We know not, and no search will make us know:
Only the event will teach us in its hour."
   He spoke; and Rustum answer'd not, but hurl'd
His spear; down from the shoulder, down it came,
As on some partridge in the corn a hawk
That long has tower'd in the airy clouds
Drops like a plummet: Sohrab saw it come,
And sprang aside, quick as a flash: the spear
Hiss'd, and went quivering down into the sand
Which it sent flying wide:—then Sohrab threw
In turn, and full struck Rustum's shield: sharp rang,
The iron plates rang sharp, but turn'd the spear.
And Rustum seiz'd his club, which none but he
Could wield: an unlopp'd trunk it was, and huge,
Still rough; like those which men in treeless plains
To build them boats fish from the flooded rivers,
Hyphasis or Hydaspes, when, high up
By their dark springs, the wind in winter-time
Hath made in Himalayan forests wrack,

And strewn the channels with torn boughs—so huge
The club which Rustum lifted now, and struck
One stroke; but again Sohrab sprang aside
Lithe as the glancing snake, and the club came
Thundering to earth, and leapt from Rustum's hand.
And Rustum follow'd his own blow, and fell
To his knees, and with his fingers clutch'd the sand:
And now might Sohrab have unsheath'd his sword,
And pierced the mighty Rustum while he lay
Dizzy, and on his knees, and choked with sand;
But he look'd on, and smil'd, nor bared his sword,
But courteously drew back, and spoke, and said:—
　　"Thou strik'st too hard: that club of thine will float
Upon the summer floods, and not my bones.
But rise, and be not wroth; not wroth am I:
No, when I see thee, wrath forsakes my soul.
Thou say'st, thou art not Rustum: be it so!
Who art thou then, that canst so touch my soul?
Boy as I am, I have seen battles too;
Have waded foremost in their bloody waves,
And heard their hollow roar of dying men;
But never was my heart thus touch'd before.
Are they from Heaven, these softenings of the heart?
O thou old warrior, let us yield to Heaven!
Come, plant we here in earth our angry spears,
And make a truce, and sit upon this sand,
And pledge each other in red wine, like friends,
And thou shalt talk to me of Rustum's deeds.
There are enough foes in the Persian host
Whom I may meet, and strike, and feel no pang;
Champions enough Afrasiab has, whom thou
Mayst fight; fight *them*, when they confront thy spear!

But oh, let there be peace 'twixt thee and me! "
 He ceased: but while he spake, Rustum had risen,
And stood erect, trembling with rage: his club
He left to lie, but had regain'd his spear,
Whose fiery point now in his mail'd right hand
Blazed bright and baleful, like that autumn-star,
The baleful sign of fevers: dust had soil'd
His stately crest, and dimm'd his glittering arms.
His breast heav'd; his lips foam'd; and twice his voice
Was chok'd with rage: at last these words broke way:—
 "Girl! nimble with thy feet, not with thy hands!
Curl'd minion, dancer, coiner of sweet words!
Fight; let me hear thy hateful voice no more!
Thou art not in Afrasiab's gardens now
With Tartar girls, with whom thou art wont to dance;
But on the Oxus-sands, and in the dance
Of battle, and with me, who make no play
Of war: I fight it out, and hand to hand.
Speak not to me of truce, and pledge, and wine!
Remember all thy valour; try thy feints
And cunning! all the pity I had is gone;
Because thou hast shamed me before both the hosts
With thy light skipping tricks, and thy girl's wiles."
 He spoke; and Sohrab kindled at his taunts,
And he too drew his sword: at once they rush'd
Together, as two eagles on one prey
Come rushing down together from the clouds,
One from the east, one from the west: their shields
Dash'd with a clang together, and a din
Rose, such as that the sinewy woodcutters
Make often in the forest's heart at morn,
Of hewing axes, crashing trees—such blows

Rustum and Sohrab on each other hail'd.
And you would say that sun and stars took part
In that unnatural conflict; for a cloud
Grew suddenly in Heaven, and dark'd the sun
Over the fighters' heads; and a wind rose
Under their feet, and moaning swept the plain,
And in a sandy whirlwind wrapp'd the pair.
In gloom they twain were wrapp'd, and they alone;
For both the on-looking hosts on either hand
Stood in broad daylight, and the sky was pure,
And the sun sparkled on the Oxus stream.
But in the gloom they fought, with bloodshot eyes
And labouring breath; first Rustum struck the shield
Which Sohrab held stiff out: the steel-spiked spear
Rent the tough plates, but fail'd to reach the skin,
And Rustum pluck'd it back with angry groan.
Then Sohrab with his sword smote Rustum's helm,
Nor clove its steel quite through; but all the crest
He shore away, and that proud horsehair plume,
Never till now defiled, sank to the dust;
And Rustum bow'd his head; but then the gloom
Grew blacker: thunder rumbled in the air,
And lightnings rent the cloud; and Ruksh, the horse,
Who stood at hand, utter'd a dreadful cry:
No horse's cry was that, most like the roar
Of some pain'd desert lion, who all day
Has trail'd the hunter's javelin in his side,
And comes at night to die upon the sand.
The two hosts heard that cry, and quaked for fear,
And Oxus curdled as it cross'd his stream.
But Sohrab heard, and quail'd not, but rush'd on,
And struck again; and again Rustum bow'd

His head; but this time all the blade, like glass,
Sprang in a thousand shivers on the helm,
And in his hand the hilt remain'd alone.
Then Rustum rais'd his head: his dreadful eyes
Glared, and he shook on high his menacing spear,
And shouted, *Rustum!* Sohrab heard that shout,
And shrank amazed; back he recoil'd one step,
And scann'd with blinking eyes the advancing form;
And then he stood bewilder'd; and he dropp'd
His covering shield, and the spear pierc'd his side.
He reel'd, and staggering back, sank to the ground.
And then the gloom dispers'd, and the wind fell,
And the bright sun broke forth, and melted all
The cloud; and the two armies saw the pair;
Saw Rustum standing, safe upon his feet,
And Sohrab, wounded, on the bloody sand.
　　Then, with a bitter smile, Rustum began:—
"Sohrab, thou thoughtest in thy mind to kill
A Persian lord this day, and strip his corpse,
And bear thy trophies to Afrasiab's tent.
Or else that the great Rustum would come down
Himself to fight, and that thy wiles would move
His heart to take a gift, and let thee go.
And then that all the Tartar host would praise
Thy courage or thy craft, and spread thy fame,
To glad thy father in his weak old age.
Fool! thou art slain, and by an unknown man!
Dearer to the red jackals shalt thou be,
Than to thy friends, and to thy father old."
　　And with a fearless mien Sohrab replied:—
"Unknown thou art; yet thy fierce vaunt is vain.
Thou dost not slay me, proud and boastful man!

No! Rustum slays me, and this filial heart.
For were I match'd with ten such men as thee,
And I were he who till to-day I was,
They should be lying here, I standing there.
But that belovèd name unnerv'd my arm—
That name, and something, I confess, in thee,
Which troubles all my heart, and made my shield
Fall; and thy spear transfix'd an unarm'd foe.
And now thou boastest, and insult'st my fate.
But hear thou this, fierce man, tremble to hear!
The mighty Rustum shall avenge my death!
My father, whom I seek through all the world,
He shall avenge my death, and punish thee! "
  As when some hunter in the spring hath found
A breeding eagle sitting on her nest,
Upon the craggy isle of a hill lake,
And pierced her with an arrow as she rose,
And follow'd her to find her where she fell
Far off;—anon her mate comes winging back
From hunting, and a great way off descries
His huddling young left sole; at that, he checks
His pinion, and with short uneasy sweeps
Circles above his eyry, with loud screams
Chiding his mate back to her nest; but she
Lies dying, with the arrow in her side,
In some far stony gorge out of his ken,
A heap of fluttering feathers—never more
Shall the lake glass her, flying over it;
Never the black and dripping precipices
Echo her stormy scream as she sails by—
As that poor bird flies home, nor knows his loss,
So Rustum knew not his own loss, but stood

Over his dying son, and knew him not.
   But with a cold, incredulous voice, he said:—
"What prate is this of fathers and revenge?
The mighty Rustum never had a son."
   And, with a failing voice, Sohrab replied:—
"Ah yes, he had! and that lost son am I.
Surely the news will one day reach his ear,
Reach Rustum, where he sits, and tarries long,
Somewhere, I know not where, but far from here;
And pierce him like a stab, and make him leap
To arms, and cry for vengeance upon thee."

MATTHEW ARNOLD

THE COMBAT BETWEEN HECTOR[1] AND AJAX[2]

(From Homer's " Iliad ")

Now Ajax braced his dazzling armour on;
Sheathed in bright steel the giant warrior shone;
He moves to combat with majestic pace:
So stalks in arms the grisly god of Thrace,[3]
When Jove to punish faithless men prepares,
And gives whole nations to the waste of wars.
Thus marched the chief, tremendous as a god:
Grimly he smiled: earth trembled as he strode:
His massy javelin quivering in his hand,
He stood, the bulwark of the Grecian band.
Through every Argive heart new transport ran;

---

[1] Hector, a son of Priam, was the most valiant of the Trojans who fought against the Greeks at Troy.

[2] Ajax the son of Telamon was, next to Achilles, the greatest of the Greek warriors.

[3] The god of war, Ares (Mars).

All Troy stood trembling at the mighty man:
E'en Hector paused; and, with new doubt oppressed,
Felt his great heart suspended in his breast.
'Twas vain to seek retreat, and vain to fear;
Himself had challenged, and his foe drew near.

Stern Telamon behind his ample shield,
As from a brazen tower, o'erlooked the field:
Huge was its orb, with seven thick folds o'ercast,
Of tough bull-hides: of solid brass the last,
(The work of Tychius, who in Hylé[1] dwell'd,
And in all arts of armoury excell'd).
This Ajax bore before his manly breast,
And, threatening, thus his adverse chief address'd.
"Hector, approach my arm and singly know
What strength thou hast, and what the Grecian foe.
Achilles shuns the fight; yet some there are,
Not void in soul, and not unskilled in war:
Let him, unactive on the sea-beat shore,
Indulge his wrath, and aid our arms no more;
Whole troops of heroes Greece has yet to boast,
And sends thee one, a sample of her host.
Such as I am, I come to prove thy might:
No more—be sudden and begin thy fight."

"O son of Telamon, thy country's Pride!
(To Ajax thus the Trojan prince replied)
Me, as a boy or woman, wouldst thou fright,
New to the field, and trembling at the fight?
Thou meet'st a chief deserving of thy arms,
To combat born, and bred amidst alarms;

[1] A small town in Greece.

159

I know to shift my ground, remount the car,
Turn, charge, and answer every call of war;
To right, to left, the dexterous lance I wield,
And bear thick battle on my sounding shield.
But open be our fight and bold each blow;
I steal no conquest from a noble foe."
He said, and rising, high above the field
Whirl'd the long lance against the sevenfold shield.
Full on the brass descending from above
Through six bull-hides the furious weapon drove,
Till in the seventh it fixed.   Then Ajax threw;
Through Hector's shield the forceful javelin flew,
His corselet enters, and his garment rends,
And glancing downwards, near his flank descends.
The wary Trojan sinks, and bending low
Beneath his buckler, disappoints the blow.
From their bor'd shields the chiefs their javelins drew,
Then close impetuous, and the charge renew;
Fierce as the mountain lions, bath'd in blood,
Or foaming boars, the terror of the wood,
At Ajax, Hector his long lance extends;
The blunted point against the buckler bends.
But Ajax, watchful as his foe drew near,
Drove through the Trojan targe the knotty spear;
It reached his neck, with matchless strength impell'd;
Spouts the black gore, and dims his shining shield.
Yet ceased not Hector thus; but stooping down,
In his strong hand upheaved a flinty stone,
Black, craggy, vast: to this his force he bends:
Full on the brazen boss the stone descends;
The hollow brass resounded with the shock:
Then Ajax seized the fragment of a rock,

Applied each nerve, and swinging round on high,
With force tempestuous, let the ruin fly;
The huge stone thundering through his buckler broke:
His slacken'd knees received the numbing stroke.
Great Hector falls, extended on the field,
His bulk supporting on the shatter'd shield,
Nor wanted heavenly aid: Apollo's might
Confirmed his sinews, and restored to fight.
And now both heroes their broad falchions drew:
In flaming circles round their heads they flew;
But then by heralds' voice the word was given,
The sacred ministers of earth and heaven:
Divine Talthybius, whom the Greeks employ,
And sage Idaeus on the part of Troy,
Between the swords their peaceful sceptres rear'd;
And first Idaeus' awful voice was heard.
"Forbear, my sons! your further force to prove;
Both dear to man, and both beloved of Jove.
To either host your matchless worth is known,
Each sounds your praise, and war is all your own.
But now the Night extends her awful shade;
The goddess parts you; be the night obeyed."
To whom great Ajax his high soul expressed:
"O sage, to Hector be these words addressed:
Let him, who first provoked our chiefs to fight,
Let him demand the sanction of the night.
If first he asked it, I content obey,
And cease the strife, when Hector shows the way."
"O first of Greeks (his noble foe rejoined),
Whom heaven adorns, superior to thy kind,
With strength of body and with worth of mind!
Now martial law commands us to forbear,

Hereafter we shall meet in glorious war;
Some future day shall lengthen out the strife,
And let the gods decide of death or life;
Since then the Night extends her gloomy shade,
And heaven enjoins it, be the night obeyed.
Return, brave Ajax, to thy Grecian friends.
And joy the nations whom thy arm defends:
As I shall glad each chief, and Trojan wife,
Who wearies heaven with vows for Hector's life.
And let us, on this memorable day,
Exchange some gift; that Greece and Troy may say,
"Not hate but glory made these chiefs contend,
And each brave foe was in his soul a friend."
With that a sword with stars of silver grac'd,
The baldric[1] studded, and the sheath enchas'd,
He gave the Greek. The generous Greek bestow'd
A radiant belt that rich with purple glow'd:
Then with majestic grace they quit the plain;
This seeks the Grecian, that the Phrygian train.

ALEXANDER POPE

[1] A warrior's sword-belt.

MORTE D'ARTHUR[1]

So all day long the noise of battle roll'd
Among the mountains by the winter sea;
Until King Arthur's table, man by man,
Had fall'n in Lyonnesse about their Lord,
King Arthur: then, because his wound was deep,

[1] Compare with Mallory's prose translation from the French which
contains a selection of the Arthurian legends.

The bold Sir Bedivere uplifted him,
Sir Bedivere, the last of all his knights,
And bore him to a chapel nigh the field,
A broken chancel with a broken cross,
That stood on a dark strait of barren land.
On one side lay the Ocean, and on one
Lay a great water, and the moon was full.
　Then spake King Arthur to Sir Bedivere:
"The sequel of to-day unsolders all
The goodliest fellowship of famous knights
Whereof this world holds record.　Such a sleep
They sleep—the men I loved.　I think that we
Shall never more, at any future time,
Delight our souls with talk of knightly deeds,
Walking about the gardens and the halls
Of Camelot, as in the days that were.
I perish by this people which I made,—
Tho' Merlin sware that I should come again
To rule once more—but let what will be, be,
I am so deeply smitten thro' the helm
That without help I cannot last till morn.
Thou therefore take my brand Excalibur,
Which was my pride: for thou rememberest how
In those old days, one summer noon, an arm
Rose up from out the bosom of the lake,
Clothed in white samite,[1] mystic, wonderful,
Holding the sword—and how I row'd across
And took it, and have worn it, like a king:
And, wheresoever I am sung or told
In aftertime, this also shall be known:
But now delay not: take Excalibur,

[1] A heavy silk fabric.

And fling him far into the middle mere:
Watch what thou seëst, and lightly bring me word."
　　To him replied the bold Sir Bedivere:
" It is not meet, Sir King, to leave thee thus,
Aidless, alone, and smitten thro' the helm.
A little thing may harm a wounded man.
Yet I thy hest will all perform at full,
Watch what I see, and lightly bring thee word."
　　So saying, from the ruin'd shrine he stept,
And in the moon athwart the place of tombs,
Where lay the mighty bones of ancient men,
Old knights, and over them the sea-wind sang
Shrill, chill, with flakes of foam.　He, stepping down
By zigzag paths, and juts of pointed rock,
Came on the shining levels of the lake.
　　There drew he forth the brand Excalibur,
And o'er him, drawing it, the winter moon,
Brightening the skirts of a long cloud, ran forth
And sparkled keen with frost against the hilt:
For all the haft twinkled with diamond sparks,
Myriads of topaz-lights, and jacinth-work
Of subtlest jewellery.　He gazed so long
That both his eyes were dazzled, as he stood,
This way and that dividing the swift mind,
In act to throw: but at the last it seem'd
Better to leave Excalibur conceal'd
There in the many-knotted waterflags,
That whistled stiff and dry about the marge.
So strode he back slow to the wounded king.
　　Then spake King Arthur to Sir Bedivere:
" Hast thou perform'd my mission which I gave?
What is it thou hast seen? or what hast heard? "

And answer made the bold Sir Bedivere:
" I heard the ripple washing in the reeds,
And the wild water lapping on the crag."
   To whom replied King Arthur, faint and pale:
" Thou hast betray'd thy nature and thy name,
Not rendering true answer, as beseem'd
   Thy feälty, nor like a noble knight:
For surer sign had follow'd, either hand,
Or voice, or else a motion of the mere.
This is a shameful thing for men to lie.
Yet now, I charge thee, quickly go again
As thou art lief and dear, and do the thing
I bad thee, watch, and lightly bring me word."
   Then went Sir Bedivere the second time
Across the ridge, and paced beside the mere,
Counting the dewy pebbles, fix'd in thought;
But when he saw the wonder of the hilt,
How curiously and strangely chased, he smote
His palms together, and he cried aloud:
   " And if indeed I cast the brand away,
Surely a precious thing, one worthy note,
Should thus be lost for ever from the earth,
Which might have pleased the eyes of many men.
What good should follow this, if this were done?
What harm, undone? deep harm to disobey,
Seeing obedience is the bond of rule.
Were it well to obey then, if a king demand
An act unprofitable, against himself?
The King is sick, and knows not what he does.
What record, or what relic of my lord
Should be to aftertime, but empty breath
And rumours of a doubt? but were this kept,

Stored in some treasure-house of mighty kings,
Some one might show it at a joust of arms,
Saying, 'King Arthur's sword, Excalibur,
Wrought by the lonely maiden of the Lake.
Nine years she wrought it, sitting in the deeps
Upon the hidden bases of the hills.'
So might some old man speak in the aftertime
To all the people, winning reverence.
But now much honour and much fame were lost."

   So spake he, clouded with his own conceit,
And hid Excalibur the second time,
And so strode back slow to the wounded King.

   Then spoke King Arthur, breathing heavily:
"What is it thou hast seen? or what hast heard?"

   And answer made the bold Sir Bedivere:
"I heard the water lapping on the crag,
And the long ripple washing in the reeds."

   To whom replied King Arthur, much in wrath:
"Ah, miserable and unkind, untrue,
Unknightly, traitor-hearted! Woe is me!
Authority forgets a dying king,
Laid widow'd of the power in his eye
That bow'd the will. I see thee what thou art,
For thou, the latest-left of all my knights,
In whom should meet the offices of all,
Thou wouldst betray me for the precious hilt;
Either from lust of gold, or like a girl
Valuing the giddy pleasure of the eyes.
Yet, for a man may fail in duty twice,
And the third time may prosper, get thee hence:
But, if thou spare to fling Excalibur,
I will arise and slay thee with my hands."

Then quickly rose Sir Bedivere, and ran,
And, leaping down the ridges lightly, plunged
Among the bulrush-beds, and clutch'd the sword,
And strongly wheel'd and threw it. The great brand
Made lightnings in the splendour of the moon,
And flashing round and round, and whirl'd in an arch,
Shot like a streamer[1] of the northern morn,
Seen where the moving isles of winter shock
By night, with noises of the northern sea.
So flash'd and fell the brand Excalibur:
But ere he dipt the surface, rose an arm
Clothed in white samite, mystic, wonderful,
And caught him by the hilt and brandish'd him
Three times and drew him under in the mere.
And lightly went the other to the King.
  Then spoke King Arthur, drawing thicker breath:
" Now see I by thine eyes that this is done.
Speak out: what is it thou hast heard, or seen? "
  And answer made the bold Sir Bedivere:
" Sir King, I closed mine eyelids, lest the gems
Should blind my purpose, for I never saw,
Nor shall see, here or elsewhere, till I die,
Not tho' I live three lives of mortal men,
So great a miracle as yonder hilt.
Then with both hands I flung him, wheeling him;
But when I look'd again, behold an arm,
Clothed in white samite, mystic, wonderful,
That caught him by the hilt, and brandish'd him
Three times, and drew him under in the mere."
  And answer made King Arthur, breathing hard:
" My end draws nigh; 'tis time that I were gone.

[1] The northern lights.

Make broad thy shoulders to receive my weight,
And bear me to the margin; yet I fear
My wound hath taken cold, and I shall die."

So saying, from the pavement he half rose,
Slowly, with pain, reclining on his arm,
And looking wistfully with wide blue eyes
As in a picture. Him Sir Bedivere
Remorsefully regarded thro' his tears,
And would have spoken, but he found not words,
Then took with care, and kneeling on one knee,
O'er both his shoulders drew the languid hands,
And rising bore him thro' the place of tombs.

But, as he walk'd, King Arthur panted hard,
Like one that feels a nightmare on his bed
When all the house is mute. So sigh'd the King,
Muttering and murmuring at his ear, " Quick, quick!
I fear it is too late, and I shall die."
But the other swiftly strode from ridge to ridge,
Clothed with his breath, and looking, as he walk'd,
Larger than human on the frozen hills.
He heard the deep behind him, and a cry
Before. His own thought drove him, like a goad.
Dry clash'd his harness in the icy caves
And barren chasms, and all to left and right
The bare black cliff clang'd round him, as he based
His feet on juts of slippery crag that rang
Sharp-smitten with the dint of armèd heels—
And on a sudden, lo! the level lake,
And the long glories of the winter moon.

Then saw they how there hove a dusky barge,
Dark as a funeral scarf from 'stem to stern,
Beneath them; and descending they were ware

That all the decks were dense with stately forms,
Black-stoled, black-hooded, like a dream—by these
Three Queens with crowns of gold—and from them rose
A cry that shiver'd to the tingling stars,
And, as it were one voice, an agony
Of lamentation, like a wind, that shrills
All night in a waste land, where no one comes,
Or hath come, since the making of the world.

   Then murmur'd Arthur, " Place me in the barge,"
And to the barge they came. There those three Queens
Put forth their hands, and took the King, and wept.
But she, that rose the tallest of them all
And fairest, laid his head upon her lap,
And loosed the shatter'd casque, and chafed his hands,
And call'd him by his name, complaining loud,
And dropping bitter tears against his brow
Striped with dark blood: for all his face was white
And colourless, and like the wither'd moon
Smote by the fresh beam of the springing east;
And all his greaves[1] and cuisses[2] dash'd with drops
Of onset; and the light and lustrous curls—
That made his forehead like a rising sun
High from the daïs-throne—were parch'd with dust;
Or, clotted into points and hanging loose,
Mix'd with the knightly growth that fringed his lips,
So like a shatter'd column lay the King;
Not like that Arthur who, with lance in rest,
From spur to plume a star of tournament,
Shot thro' the lists at Camelot, and charged
Before the eyes of ladies and of kings.

---

[1] Armour to protect the legs.
[2] Armour to protect the thighs.

Then loudly cried the bold Sir Bedivere:
" Ah! my Lord Arthur, whither shall I go?
Where shall I hide my forehead and my eyes?
For now I see the true old times are dead,
When every morning brought a noble chance,
And every chance brought out a noble knight.
Such times have been not since the light that led
The holy Elders[1] with the gift of myrrh.
But now the whole ROUND TABLE is dissolved
Which was an image of the mighty world;
And I, the last, go forth companionless,
And the days darken round me, and the years,
Among new men, strange faces, other minds."

And slowly answered Arthur from the barge:
" The old order changeth, yielding place to new,
And God fulfils Himself in many ways,
Lest one good custom should corrupt the world.
Comfort thyself: what comfort is in me?
I have lived my life, and that which I have done
May He within Himself make pure! but thou,
If thou shouldst never see my face again,
Pray for my soul. More things are wrought by prayer
Than this world dreams of. Wherefore, let thy voice
Rise like a fountain for me night and day.
For what are men better than sheep or goats
That nourish a blind life within the brain,
If, knowing God, they lift not hands of prayer
Both for themselves and those who call them friend?
For so the whole round earth is every way
Bound by gold chains about the feet of God.
But now farewell. I am going a long way

[1] The Magi.

With these thou seëst—if indeed I go—
(For all my mind is clouded with a doubt)
To the island-valley of Avilion;
Where falls not hail, or rain, or any snow,
Nor ever wind blows loudly; but it lies
Deep-meadow'd, happy, fair with orchard-lawns
And bowery hollows crown'd with summer sea,
Where I will heal me of my grievous wound."
  So said he, and the barge with oar and sail
Moved from the brink, like some full-breasted swan
That, fluting a wild carol ere her death,
Ruffles her pure cold plume, and takes the flood
With swarthy webs. Long stood Sir Bedivere
Revolving many memories, till the hull
Look'd one black dot against the verge of dawn,
And on the mere the wailing died away.

LORD TENNYSON

LIFE, DEATH AND BEYOND

HEY NONNY NO!

Hey nonny no!
Men are fools that wish to die!
Is't not fine to dance and sing
When the bells of death do ring?
Is't not fine to swim in wine,
And turn upon the toe
And sing hey nonny no,
When the winds blow and the seas flow?
Hey nonny no!

ANONYMOUS

SWEET CONTENT

Art thou poor, yet hast thou golden slumbers?
O sweet content!
Art thou rich, yet is thy mind perplex'd?
O punishment!
Dost thou laugh to see how fools are vex'd
To add to golden numbers golden numbers?
O sweet content, O sweet, O sweet content!

Work apace, apace, apace, apace;
Honest labour bears a lovely face;
Then hey nonny nonny—hey nonny nonny!

Canst drink the waters of the crispèd spring?
    O sweet content!
Swimm'st thou in wealth, yet sink'st in thine own tears?
    O punishment!
Then he that patiently want's burden bears,
No burden bears, but is a king, a king!
O sweet content, O sweet, O sweet content!
    Work apace, apace, apace, apace;
    Honest labour bears a lovely face;
    Then hey nonny nonny—hey nonny nonny!

THOMAS DEKKER

THE PATRIOT

It was roses, roses, all the way,
    With myrtle mixed in my path like mad:
The house-roofs seemed to heave and sway,
    The church-spires flamed, such flags they had,
A year ago on this very day.

The air broke into a mist with bells,
    The old walls rocked with the crowd and cries.
Had I said, " Good folk, mere noise repels—
    " But give me your sun from yonder skies! "
They had answered, " And afterward, what else? "

Alack, it was I who leaped at the sun
    To give it my loving friends to keep!

173

Nought man could do, have I left undone:
  And you see my harvest, what I reap
This very day, now a year is run.

There's nobody on the house-tops now—
  Just a palsied few at the windows set;
For the best of the sight is, all allow,
  At the Shambles' Gate—or, better yet,
By the very scaffold's foot, I trow.

I go in the rain, and, more than needs,
  A rope cuts both my wrists behind;
And I think, by the feel, my forehead bleeds,
  For they fling, whoever has a mind,
Stones at me for my year's misdeeds.

Thus I entered, and thus I go!
  In triumphs, people have dropped down dead.
"Paid by the world, what dost thou owe
  "Me?"—God might question; now instead,
'Tis God shall repay: I am safer so.

ROBERT BROWNING

ON THE LATE MASSACRE IN PIEDMONT

Avenge, O Lord! Thy slaughter'd Saints,[1] whose bones
Lie scatter'd on the Alpine mountains cold;
Ev'n them who kept Thy truth so pure of old
When all our fathers worship't stocks and stones

---

[1] The Protestants who were murdered in Piedmont in 1655.

Forget not: in Thy book record their groans
Who were Thy sheep, and in their ancient fold
Slain by the bloody Piedmontese, that roll'd
Mother with infant down the rocks. Their moans

The vales redoubl'd to the hills, and they
To Heav'n. Their martyr'd blood and ashes sow
O'er all the Italian fields, where still doth sway
The triple tyrant; that from these may grow
A hunder'd-fold, who, having learnt Thy way,
Early may fly the Babylonian woe.

JOHN MILTON

THE WOOD, THE WEED, THE WAG

Three things there be that prosper up apace,
　And flourish, while they grow asunder far;
But on a day, they meet all in one place,
　And when they meet, they one another mar.

And they be these: the Wood, the Weed, the Wag:—
　The Wood is that which makes the gallow-tree;
The Weed is that which strings the hangman's bag;
　The Wag, my pretty knave, betokeneth thee.

Mark well, dear boy, whilst these assemble not,
　Green springs the tree, hemp grows, the wag is wild;
But when they meet, it makes the timber rot,
　It frets the halter, and it chokes the child.
Then bless thee, and beware, and let us pray,
We part not with thee at this meeting day.

SIR WALTER RALEIGH

LA BELLE DAME SANS MERCI

" O, what can ail thee, Knight-at-arms,
Alone and palely loitering?
The sedge is wither'd from the lake,
And no birds sing.

O, what can ail thee, Knight-at-arms,
So haggard and so woe-begone?
The squirrel's granary is full,
And the harvest's done.

I see a lily on thy brow
With anguish moist and fever dew,
And on thy cheek a fading rose
Fast withereth too."

" I met a lady in the meads
Full beautiful—a faery's child,
Her hair was long, her foot was light,
And her eyes were wild.

I set her on my pacing steed,
And nothing else saw all day long,
For sidelong would she bend and sing
A faery's song.

I made a garland for her head,
And bracelets too, and fragrant zone;
She look'd at me as she did love,
And made sweet moan.

She found me roots of relish sweet,
And honey wild and manna dew,
And sure in language strange she said
‘ I love thee true.’

She took me to her elfin grot,
And there she wept and sigh’d full sore;
And there I shut her wild wild eyes
With kisses four.

And there she lullèd me asleep,
And there I dream’d—Ah! woe betide!
The latest dream I ever dream’d
On the cold hillside.

I saw pale kings and princes too,
Pale warriors, death-pale were they all:
Who cried—‘ La belle Dame sans merci
Hath thee in thrall! ’

I saw their starv’d lips in the gloam
With horrid warning gapèd wide,
And I awoke and found me here
On the cold hillside.

And this is why I sojourn here
Alone and palely loitering,
Though the sedge is wither’d from the lake,
And no birds sing.”

JOHN KEATS

¹THE DESCENT OF ODIN²

Uprose the king of men with speed,
And saddled straight his coal-black steed:
Down the yawning steep he rode,
That leads to Hela's³ drear abode.
Him the Dog of Darkness spied;
His shaggy throat he open'd wide,
While from his jaws, with carnage fill'd,
Foam and human gore distill'd:
Hoarse he bays with hideous din,
Eyes that glow, and fangs that grin;
And long pursues, with fruitless yell,
The Father of the powerful spell.
Onward still his way he takes,
(The groaning earth beneath him shakes,)
Till full before his fearless eyes
The portals nine of Hell arise.

Right against the eastern gate,
By the moss-grown pile he sate;
Where long of yore to sleep was laid
The dust of the prophetic Maid.
Facing to the northern clime,
Thrice he trac'd the Runic⁴ rhyme;

¹ Compare with Matthew Arnold's " Balder Dead." Both poems are based on a Norse Saga.
² The father of the Norse gods.
³ The daughter of Loki. She ruled the Land of the Mist where dwell the ghosts of those not slain in battle.
⁴ Words written in runes, a special kind of writing used by the Norsemen.

Thrice pronounc'd, in accents dread,
The thrilling verse that wakes the Dead;
Till from out the hollow ground
Slowly breath'd a sullen sound.

PROPHETESS:

What call unknown, what charms, presume
To break the quiet of the tomb?
Who thus afflicts my troubled sprite,
And drags me from the realms of night?
Long on these mould'ring bones have beat
The winter's snow, the summer's heat,
The drenching dews, and driving rain!
Let me, let me sleep again.
Who is he, with voice unblest,
That calls me from the bed of rest?

ODIN:

A Traveller, to thee unknown,
Is he that calls, a Warrior's Son.
Thou the deeds of light shalt know;
Tell me what is done below,
For whom yon glitt'ring board is spread,
Drest for whom yon golden bed?

PROPHETESS:

Mantling in the goblet see
The pure bev'rage of the bee:
O'er it hangs the shield of gold;
'Tis the drink of Balder[1] bold:

[1] The noble son of Odin, shot by his blind brother, Hoder, at the instigation of Loki, the evil god.

Balder's head to death is giv'n.
Pain can reach the Sons of Heav'n!
Unwilling I my lips unclose;
Leave me, leave me to repose.

ODIN:

Once again my call obey,
Prophetess, arise, and say,
What dangers Odin's Child await,
Who the Author of his fate?

PROPHETESS:

In Hoder's hand the Hero's doom;
His brother sends him to the tomb.
Now my weary lips I close:
Leave me, leave me to repose.

ODIN:

Prophetess, my spell obey,
Once again arise, and say,
Who th' Avenger of his guilt,
By whom shall Hoder's blood be spilt?

PROPHETESS:

In the caverns of the west,
By Odin's fierce embrace comprest,
A wond'rous Boy shall Rinda bear,
Who ne'er shall comb his raven-hair,
Nor wash his visage in the stream,
Nor see the sun's departing beam,
Till he on Hoder's corse shall smile

Flaming on the fun'ral pile.
Now my weary lips I close:
Leave me, leave me to repose.

ODIN:

Yet awhile my call obey;
Prophetess, awake, and say,
What Virgins these, in speechless woe,
That bend to earth their solemn brow,
That their flaxen tresses tear,
And snowy veils that float in air?
Tell me whence their sorrows rose:
Then I leave thee to repose.

PROPHETESS:

Ha! no Traveller art thou,
King of Men,[1] I know thee now;
Mightiest of a mighty line—

ODIN:

No boding Maid of skill divine
Art thou, nor Prophetess of good;
But mother of the giant brood!

PROPHETESS:

Hie thee hence, and boast at home,
That never shall Enquirer come
To break my iron-sleep again;
Till Lok has burst his tenfold chain;

[1] Odin (or Woden).

181

Never, till substantial Night
Has reassum'd her ancient right;
Till wrapt in flames, in ruin hurl'd,
Sinks the fabric of the world.

THOMAS GRAY

BALDER'S FUNERAL

(From " Balder Dead ")

But now the sun had pass'd the height of Heaven,
And soon had all that day been spent in wail;
But then the Father[1] of the ages said:—
  " Ye Gods, there well may be too much of wail!
Bring now the gather'd wood to Balder's ship;
Heap on the deck the logs, and build the pyre."
  But when the Gods and Heroes heard, they brought
The wood to Balder's ship, and built a pile,
Full the deck's breadth, and lofty; then the corpse
Of Balder on the highest top they laid,
With Nanna[2] on his right, and on his left
Hoder, his brother, whom his own hand slew.
And they set jars of wine and oil to lean
Against the bodies, and stuck torches near,
Splinters of pine-wood, soak'd with turpentine;
And brought his arms and gold, and all his stuff,
And slew the dogs who at his table fed,
And his horse, Balder's horse, whom most he loved,
And placed them on the pyre, and Odin threw
A last choice gift thereon, his golden ring.

[1] Odin.
[2] Balder's wife.

The mast they fixt, and hoisted up the sails,
Then they put fire to the wood; and Thor[1]
Set his stout shoulder hard against the stern
To push the ship through the thick sand;—sparks flew
From the deep trench she plough'd, so strong a God
Furrow'd it; and the water gurgled in.
And the ship floated on the waves, and rock'd.
But in the hills a strong east-wind arose,
And came down moaning to the sea; first squalls
Ran black o'er the sea's face, then steady rush'd
The breeze, and fill'd the sails, and blew the fire.
And wreathed in smoke the ship stood out to sea.
Soon with a roaring rose the mighty fire,
And the pile crackled; and between the logs
Sharp quivering tongues of flame shot out, and leapt,
Curling and darting, higher, until they lick'd
The summit of the pile, the dead, the mast,
And ate the shrivelling sails; but still the ship
Drove on, ablaze above her hull with fire.
And the Gods stood upon the beach, and gazed.
And while they gazed, the sun went lurid down
Into the smoke-wrapt sea, and night came on.
Then the wind fell, with night, and there was calm;
But through the dark they watch'd the burning ship
Still carried o'er the distant waters on,
Farther and farther, like an eye of fire.
And long, in the far dark, blazed Balder's pile;
But fainter, as the stars rose high, it flared,
The bodies were consumed, ash choked the pile,
And as, in a decaying winter-fire,
A charr'd log, falling, makes a shower of sparks—

[1] Son of Odin and god of war.

So with a shower of sparks the pile fell in,
Reddening the sea around; and all was dark.

MATTHEW ARNOLD

PROSPERO'S FAREWELL
(*From " The Tempest "*)

Our revels now are ended. These our actors,
As I foretold you, were all spirits, and
Are melted into air, into thin air:
And, like the baseless fabric of this vision,
The cloud-capp'd towers, the gorgeous palaces,
The solemn temples, the great globe itself,
Yea, all which it inherit, shall dissolve
And, like this insubstantial pageant faded,
Leave not a rack behind. We are such stuff
As dreams are made on; and our little life
Is rounded with a sleep.

WILLIAM SHAKESPEARE

THE SUMMONING OF SATAN'S COUNCIL
(*From " Paradise Lost "*)

Meanwhile the wingèd Heralds, by command
Of sovran power, with awful ceremony
And trumpet's sound, throughout the host proclaim
A solemn council forthwith to be held
At Pandemonium,[1] the high capital

[1] The great hall where all the devils meet.

Of Satan and his peers. Their summons called
From every band and squarèd regiment
By place or choice the worthiest: they anon
With hundreds and with thousands trooping came
Attended. All access was thronged; the gates
And porches wide, but chief the spacious hall
(Though like a covered field, where champions bold
Wont ride in armed, and at the Soldan's chair
Defied the best of Panim[1] chivalry
To mortal combat, or career with lance),
Thick swarmed, both on the ground and in the air,
Brushed with the hiss of rustling wings. As bees
In spring-time, when the Sun with Taurus rides,
Pour forth their populous youth about the hive
In clusters; they among fresh dews and flowers
Fly to and fro, or on the smoothèd plank,
The suburb of their straw-built citadel,
New rubbed with balm, expatiate and confer
Their state-affairs: so thick the aery crowd
Swarmed and were straitened; till, the signal given,
Behold a wonder! They but now who seemed
In bigness to surpass Earth's giant sons,
Now less than smallest dwarfs, in a narrow room
Throng numberless—like that pygmean race
Beyond the Indian mount; or faery elves,
Whose midnight revels, by a forest-side
Or fountain, some belated peasant sees,
Or dreams he sees, while overhead the Moon
Sits arbitress, and nearer to the Earth
Wheels her pale course: they, on their mirth and dance
Intent, with jocund music charm his ear;

[1] Pagan.

At once with joy and fear his heart rebounds.
Thus incorporeal Spirits to smallest forms
Reduced their shapes immense, and were at large,
Though without number still, amidst the hall
Of that infernal court. But far within,
And in their own dimensions like themselves,
The great Seraphic Lords and Cherubim
In close recess and secret conclave sat,
A thousand demi-gods on golden seats,
Frequent and full. After short silence then,
And summons read, the great consult began.

JOHN MILTON

INDEX OF AUTHORS

INDEX OF AUTHORS

INDEX OF AUTHORS

INDEX OF AUTHORS

INDEX OF FIRST LINES

Poetic Devices.

Simile = a comparison.

Metaphor = one thing spoken of in terms
of another.

Personification = an inatimate object spoke
of as a person.

Alliteration. = the repetition of the same
sound at the begining of
stressed words in one line

CUBS AT PLAY

'The Scouts are stuck,' yelled Nobby from the bank.

True enough, the heavier Scout crew was grounded in the shallows. They were stuck, hard and fast.

Akela glanced over his shoulder. The Scouts were in no danger, but now the Cubs, afloat in deep water, had a real advantage. They had only a hundred metres to go to the finishing line. There was a possibility that they could reach it before the Scouts got themselves afloat again and caught up.

'Heave! Heave! Heave! Heave! Heave!' yelled Akela, at the top of his voice, as if everyone in the world was deaf to his words.

Also in Beaver by Stephen Andrews

Cubs With a Difference
Cubs Away
Cubs on Saturday